Dr Eliot Attridge

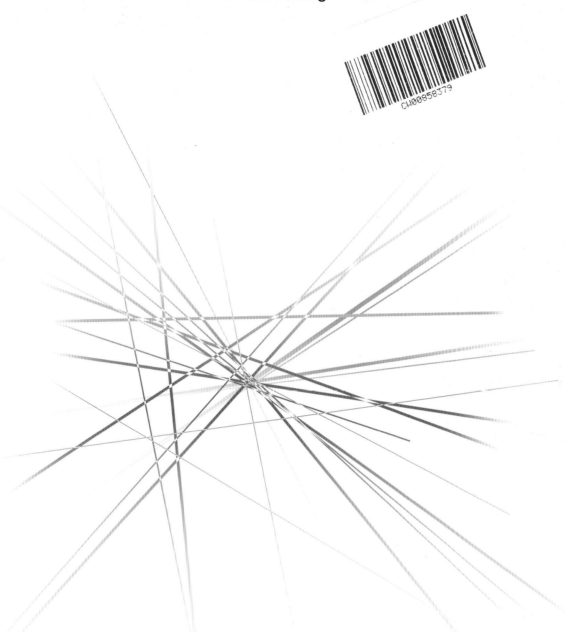

ESSENTIALS

OCR Twenty First Century
GCSE Biology
Revision Guide

Contents

Contents

Module B5: Growth and Development

Module B6: Brain and Mind

Module B7: Further Biology

This revision guide has been written and developed to help you get the most out of your revision.

This guide covers both Foundation and Higher Tier content.

HT Content that will only be tested on the Higher Tier papers appears in a pale yellow tinted box labelled with the **HT** symbol.

- The **coloured page headers** clearly identify the separate units, so that you can revise for each exam separately.
- There are **practice questions** at the end of each unit so you can test yourself on what you've just learned. (The answers are given on pages 110–111 so you can mark your own answers.)

- You'll find **key words** in a yellow box on each two-page spread. They are also highlighted in colour within the text; Higher Tier key words are highlighted in orange. Make sure you know and understand all these words before moving on!
- There's a **glossary** at the back of the book. It contains all the key words from throughout the book so you can check any definitions you're not sure about.
- The **tick boxes** on the contents page let you track your revision progress: simply put a tick in the box next to each topic when you're confident that you know it.
- Don't just read the guide, **learn actively**! Constantly test yourself without looking at the text.

Good luck with your exams!

Life on Earth

Evolution by Natural Selection

Evolution…
- is the slow, continual change over generations
- may result in a new species which is **better adapted** to its environment
- occurs due to natural selection, when individuals have characteristics which improve their chances of survival.

Four key points about natural selection:
1. Individuals show **variation**, i.e. differences due to their genes.
2. There's competition for food and mates. Also, disease and predators keep population sizes constant in spite of many offspring.
3. Those better adapted are more likely to survive and reproduce whilst others die out. This is 'survival of the fittest'.
4. Survivors pass on genes to their offspring, resulting in an improved organism evolving over generations.

Natural selection relies on variation caused by the environment and genes. However, only a **genetic variation** can be passed on. For example, if you lost a finger, this characteristic wouldn't be passed on. This is environmental variation.

Increased competition has seen grey squirrels outnumber red squirrels.

HT Peppered Moths are naturally pale and speckled, so are well camouflaged against silver birch trees.

However, during the Industrial Revolution, air pollution discoloured the trees with soot and natural selection led to a **new variety** of Peppered Moth:
1. **Variation** – some moths were naturally darker due to their genes.
2. **Competition** – darker-coloured and paler moths had to compete for food.
3. **Better adapted** – darker moths were better camouflaged against the blackened trees and buildings. Paler moths were seen by birds and were eaten.
4. **Passing on genes** – darker moths were more likely to survive and breed, passing on their genes for darker pigmentation.

The Clean Air Act reduced air pollution which meant more silver birch trees stayed 'silver'. This gave the pale variety an advantage so numbers began to grow again. Today, the presence of the pale variety is regarded as a clean air marker.

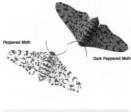

Peppered Moth

Dark Peppered Moth

Key Words

Competition • Environmental variation • Evolution • Mutation • Natural selection • Selective breeding • Survival of the fittest

HT Gene Mutation

A change in a gene is a mutation. Occasionally, mutations can alter the properties of a **protein** and can influence the **development** of an organism.

If this happens in a **sex cell** then the mutated gene can be passed on to the offspring, which may show **new characteristics**.

A new species can be produced through the combined effects of **mutations**, **environmental changes** and **natural selection**.

Example of a Gene Mutation

These three bases produce cysteine.

This base has mutated so now the amino acid tyrosine is produced.

Selective Breeding

Selective breeding is when animals with certain traits are mated to produce offspring with certain desirable characteristics. Selective breeding can produce two outcomes:

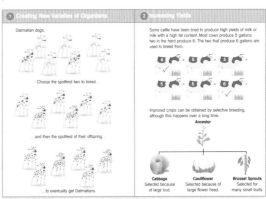

1 Creating New Varieties of Organisms

Dalmatian dogs.

Choose the spottiest two to breed.

…and then the spottiest of their offspring

…to eventually get Dalmatians.

2 Increasing Yields

Some cattle have been bred to produce high yields of milk or milk with a high fat content. Most cows produce 5 gallons; two in the herd produce 6. The two that produce 6 gallons are used to breed from.

Improved crops can be obtained by selective breeding, although this happens over a long time.

Ancestor

Cabbage
Selected because of large bud.

Cauliflower
Selected because of large flower head.

Brussel Sprouts
Selected for many small buds.

You and Your Genes

Variation

Differences between individuals of the same species are called **variation**.

Variation may be due to…
- **genetic factors**
- **environmental factors**.

Genetic Causes   Environmental Causes

Genetic Information

Genes carry the information needed for you to develop. **Different genes** control **different characteristics**, e.g. the colour of your eyes.

Genes…
- occur in long strings called **chromosomes**
- are located inside the **nucleus** of **every cell**.

Chromosomes are made of **DNA** (deoxyribonucleic acid) molecules. DNA molecules are…
- made up of **two strands**
- coiled to form a **double helix**.

DNA molecules form a complete set of instructions for…
- how the organism should be constructed
- how each cell should function.

Genes are sections of DNA. Genes **control the development** of different characteristics by **issuing instructions** to the cell. The cell carries out these instructions by producing **proteins**.

HT The proteins formed inside a cell can be…
- **structural proteins** (for cell growth or repair)
- **enzymes** (to speed up chemical reactions).

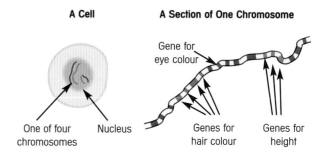

A Cell   A Section of One Chromosome

Gene for eye colour

One of four chromosomes   Nucleus   Genes for hair colour   Genes for height

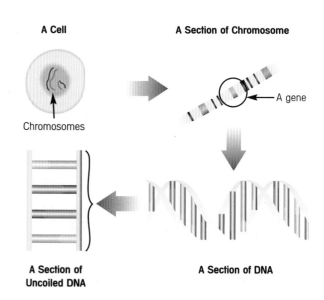

A Cell   A Section of Chromosome

Chromosomes   A gene

A Section of Uncoiled DNA   A Section of DNA

Genetic Modification

All organisms have DNA. This means it's possible to introduce genetic information from one organism into another. This will produce a new **combination** of genes and characteristics. It is called **genetic modification**.

Key Words

Allele • Chromosome • DNA • Gene • Nucleus • Protein • Variation

Chromosomes

Chromosomes normally come in **pairs**:

- Both chromosomes in a pair have the **same sequence** of genes, i.e. the same genes in the same place.
- Different species have different numbers of pairs. **Human cells** contain **23 pairs** of chromosomes (46 in total).

Pairs of Chromosomes in a Human Male

Sperm		Egg		Fertilised Egg Cell
〜●	+	●	=	●
23 chromosomes	+	23 chromosomes	=	46 chromosomes (23 pairs) − half from mother (egg) and half from father (sperm)

Sex cells contain single chromosomes. In humans they have a total of 23 chromosomes; half the number of a normal body cell.

1 2 3 4 5

6 7 8 9 10 11

12 13 14 15 16 17

18 19 20 21 22 XY

Alleles

A gene can have **different versions**, called **alleles**. For example, the gene for eye colour has two alleles: brown and blue. For each gene, you inherit one allele from your father and one from your mother. This is why you can have similarities to **both** of your parents.

You can inherit two alleles that are the same or two that are different. Brothers and sisters can **randomly inherit** different combinations for all the different genes, which is why they can be very different.

Alleles can be **dominant** or **recessive**.

Dominant allele − controls the development of a characteristic even if it's present on only one chromosome in a pair.

Recessive allele − controls the development of a characteristic only if a dominant allele isn't present, i.e. if the recessive allele is present on both chromosomes in a pair.

Genetic Diagrams

Genetic diagrams are used to show all the possible combinations of alleles and outcomes for a particular gene. They use...

- **capital letters** for **dominant** alleles
- **lower case letters** for **recessive** alleles.

You can also use a **family tree** to identify how you have inherited a characteristic, such as your hair colour.

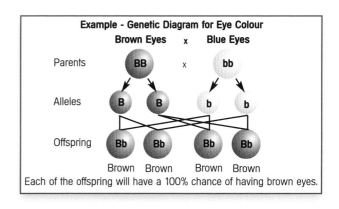

Example - Genetic Diagram for Eye Colour

Brown Eyes x Blue Eyes

Parents BB x bb

Alleles B B b b

Offspring Bb Bb Bb Bb

Brown Brown Brown Brown

Each of the offspring will have a 100% chance of having brown eyes.

You and Your Genes

Genetics and Lifestyle

Most characteristics are determined by several genes working together. However, they can be influenced by **environmental factors**. For example, your height is determined by a variety of genes, but factors like diet can also affect it.

Poor diet can lead to **disease**. For example, a fatty diet can increase the risk of heart disease.

It's possible to limit the chances of getting certain diseases by making **lifestyle changes**.

Sex Chromosomes

One of the 23 pairs of **chromosomes** in a human body cell is the **sex chromosomes**:
- In **females** the sex chromosomes are **identical**; they are both **X** chromosomes.
- In **males** they are **different**; there is an **X** and a **Y** chromosome. The Y chromosome is much shorter than the X chromosome.

Male

X Y

Female

X X

Half the sperm carry X chromosomes and half carry Y chromosomes.

All the eggs carry X chromosomes.

X

Y

X

X X

X Y

If an X sperm fertilises the egg, a girl is produced.

If a Y sperm fertilises the egg, a boy is produced.

HT The sex of an individual is determined by a gene on the **Y chromosome** called the **sex-determining region Y** (SRY) gene.

If the gene isn't present, i.e. if there are two **X chromosomes** present, the embryo will develop into a female.

If the gene is present, i.e. if there is an X chromosome and a Y chromosome, **testes** begin to develop.

After six weeks the testes start producing a hormone called **androgen**. Specialised **receptors** in the developing embryo detect the androgen and male reproductive organs begin to grow.

Sometimes the Y chromosome is present but androgen isn't detected. When this happens…
- the embryo develops female sex organs apart from the uterus
- the baby has a female body but is **infertile**.

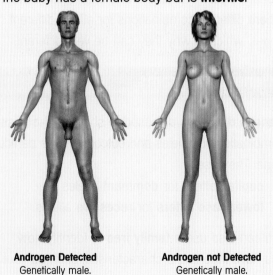

Androgen Detected
Genetically male.
Appears male.

Androgen not Detected
Genetically male.
Appears female but has no uterus.

Huntington's Disorder

Most characteristics are governed by a range of genes, so one 'faulty' **allele** may not affect the overall outcome. However, although rare, some disorders are caused by a single allele, e.g. **Huntington's disorder**.

Huntington's disorder (HD)…

- is a genetic disorder affecting the **central nervous system**. It's caused by a 'faulty' gene on the fourth pair of chromosomes
- damages the brain's **nerve cells**
- causes gradual changes, which develop into symptoms including **involuntary movement** and **dementia**
- is incurable, leading to premature death.

Symptoms of HD can **differ**, even within the same family. Symptoms normally develop in adulthood,

which means sufferers may already have passed it on to their children. Only one parent needs to pass on the gene for a child to **inherit** it. Everyone who inherits the HD allele will develop the disorder because the allele is **dominant**.

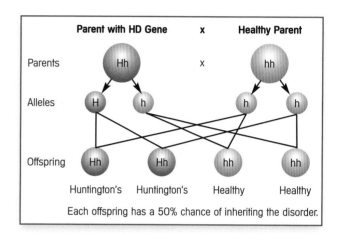

Each offspring has a 50% chance of inheriting the disorder.

Cystic Fibrosis

Cystic fibrosis affects **cell membranes**, causing a thick, sticky mucus, especially in the **lungs**, **gut** and **pancreas**.

Symptoms can include **weight loss**, **coughs**, **repeated chest infections**, **salty sweat** and **abnormal faeces**.

There's no cure, but scientists have identified the allele that causes it.

Unlike Huntington's disorder, the cystic fibrosis allele is **recessive**. So, if an individual has one **recessive allele**, they will not have the disorder's characteristics.

However, they are called **carriers** because they can pass the allele on to their children.

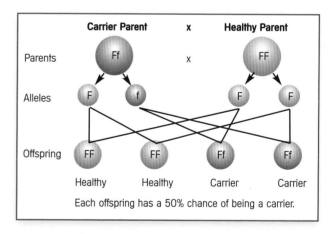

Each offspring has a 50% chance of being a carrier.

Key Words

Allele • Chromosome • Cystic fibrosis • Huntington's disorder • Sex-determining region Y

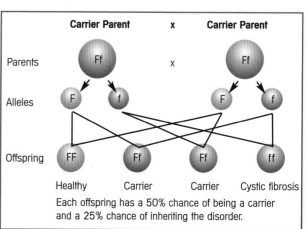

Each offspring has a 50% chance of being a carrier and a 25% chance of inheriting the disorder.

You and Your Genes

Genetic Testing

It's possible to test a person for a faulty **allele**. If the tests are positive, couples must choose whether to have children and risk passing on the disorder, to **adopt** a child instead, or to use **embryo selection**.

Fetuses can also be tested. If the faulty allele is present in a developing fetus, parents may decide whether to terminate the pregnancy.

Testing the Fetus

There are two ways of removing cells so that a **genetic test** can be carried out on a fetus.

Amniocentesis testing is carried out at 14–16 weeks.
1. A needle is inserted into the uterus, taking care to avoid the fetus.
2. A sample of **amniotic fluid**, carrying cells from the fetus, is extracted and tested.
3. If the test is positive, the pregnancy could be terminated.
4. There's a 0.5% chance of the test causing a miscarriage, and a small chance of infection.

Chorionic villus testing is carried out at 8–10 weeks.
1. A special catheter is inserted through the vagina and cervix until it reaches the **placenta**.
2. Part of the placenta has **chorionic villi**, which are made from **fetal cells**. Samples are removed and tested.
3. If the test is positive the pregnancy can be terminated much earlier than with amniocentesis testing.
4. The chance of miscarriage is much higher at 2%, but there's virtually no risk of infection.

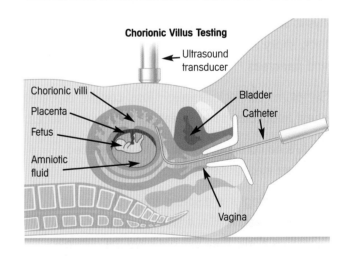

Amniocentesis Testing

Placenta
Fetus
Uterus
Amniotic fluid
Cervix

Chorionic Villus Testing

Ultrasound transducer
Chorionic villi
Placenta
Fetus
Amniotic fluid
Bladder
Catheter
Vagina

Reliability

As no test is 100% reliable, genetic testing on a fetus can have a number of outcomes, as the table shows.

False negatives are rare and **false positives** even rarer. But a false positive result means that parents may choose to terminate the pregnancy when the fetus is in fact healthy.

Outcome	Test result	Reality
True Positive	Fetus **has** the disorder	Fetus **has** the disorder
True Negative	Fetus **does not** have the disorder	Fetus **does not** have the disorder
False Positive	Fetus **has** the disorder	Fetus **does not** have the disorder
False Negative	Fetus **does not** have the disorder	Fetus **has** the disorder

The Implications of Genetic Testing

Before genetic testing can become common practice, the following questions should be addressed:
- How can mistakes be prevented?
- Is it right to interfere with nature?
- Who has the right to decide if a disorder is worth living with?

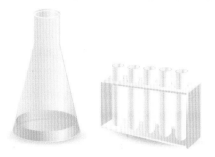

HT There is always a difference between what **can** be done and what **should** be done. Governments may have the ability to test, but should they be allowed?

Potentially, genetic testing could be used to produce **genetic profiles** containing information such as…
- your **ethnicity**
- whether you're **susceptible** to certain conditions or diseases.

It's been suggested that babies could be **screened at birth**, allowing doctors…
- to tailor healthcare and prevent problems
- to stop genetic disorders from being passed on, eliminating them completely.

One view is that this would mean less suffering and the money currently spent on treatment could be used elsewhere. The **opposing view** is that these disorders are natural and it would be wrong to eliminate them.

Storing genetic information raises questions about **confidentiality**. For example, it could be used to **discriminate** and people may be turned down for jobs if they are found to have a **higher risk** of illness.

The availability of money and trained staff affects what can be done, so different countries develop different policies depending on their economy.

Embryo Selection

Embryo selection is another way of preventing babies from having genetic disorders. Embryos can be produced by *in vitro* **fertilisation** (IVF):

1. **Ova** are harvested from the mother and fertilised.
2. The embryos are tested for the faulty allele.
3. Healthy embryos are **implanted** into the **uterus**. The pregnancy proceeds as normal.

HT The procedure for embryo selection is called Pre-implantation Genetic Diagnosis (PGD):

1. After fertilisation the embryos are allowed to **divide** into 8 cells before a single cell is removed from each one for testing
2. The cells are tested to see if they carry the alleles for a **specific genetic disorder**.

Embryo selection is **controversial**:
- Some people believe it's **unnatural**.
- There are concerns that people could select certain characteristics, such as eye colour, sex, etc., in advance (pre-selection).

Pre-selection of a baby's characteristics could **reduce variation**. For example, if most people selected blue eyes for their baby, the brown eye allele could disappear in time.

Key Words

Allele • Fetus • Genetic test • *In vitro* fertilisation • Pre-implantation Genetic Diagnosis

You and Your Genes

Gene Therapy

Gene therapy…
- is a potential treatment for certain **genetic disorders**
- involves inserting 'healthy' genes into cells in order to treat a disease.

The most common method uses genes from healthy people.

The genes are inserted into a **modified virus**, which infects the patient. The genes become part of the patient's cells, correcting the faulty allele.

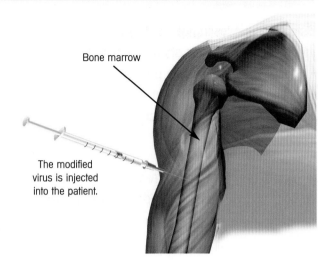

Bone marrow

The modified virus is injected into the patient.

Gene Therapy and Ethics

New procedures raise questions. Some **can** be answered by further **scientific research**, e.g:
- Does it work and is it safe? What are the potential risks and side effects?
- How do you target cells?
- Can gene therapy cause cancer?

Some questions **can't** be answered by science:
- Is it right to manipulate genes this way?
- Where do we draw the line between repairing damage and making improvements?
- Do we have the right to decide for future generations?

These questions address the same **ethical** issue: **is gene therapy acceptable**? To answer this we need to decide what's right and what's wrong.

Society has **common beliefs**. For example, most people agree that murder is wrong. However, there are different views about what's acceptable, and about what should be done.

We shouldn't decide whether gene therapy is right or wrong by simply counting the arguments. The **quality** of each argument is more important. For example, you may believe it's more important to save lives than worry about an 'unnatural' procedure.

Decisions about ethical issues are normally based on what will **benefit the majority**. This means some people will always object to a decision.

Arguments For Gene Therapy	Arguments Against Gene Therapy
• It's an **acceptable procedure**, comparable to vaccination, and less invasive than surgery.	• It's **unnatural** and **morally wrong** to change people's genes and DNA.
• People with genetic conditions can need a lifetime of care and treatment. Gene therapy will **improve lives** and free up resources.	• It's **experimental** and we don't know the long-term effects.
• Some conditions reduce life expectancy. Gene therapy will allow a **normal life**.	• It will need to be tested on humans, which isn't safe as we don't know the **side effects**.

Asexual Reproduction

Bacteria and other **single-cell organisms** can reproduce by dividing to form two 'new' individuals. The new individuals are **clones** (genetically identical to the parent).

This is **asexual reproduction**. Most plants and some animals can reproduce in this way.

Variation in organisms that reproduce **asexually** is normally only caused by **environmental factors**.

Clones can occur naturally:
- The cells of an embryo sometimes **separate**.
- The two new embryos develop into **identical twins**.

HT **Animal clones** can be produced **artificially**:
- The **nucleus** from an adult body cell is transferred into an empty (nucleus removed) unfertilised egg cell.
- The new individual will have exactly the same genetic information as the donor.

Cell Division During Asexual Reproduction

Parental cell with two pairs of chromosomes.

Each chromosome replicates itself.

The copies are pulled apart. Cell now divides for the only time.

Each 'daughter' cell has the same number of chromosomes and contains the same genes as the parental cell.

Stem Cells

Most organisms are made up of various **specialised** cells with **different structures**. In the early stages of development, cells aren't specialised. These are called **stem cells**.

Stem cells have the potential to develop into any type of cell. They can potentially be used to replace damaged tissues, e.g. in patients with **Parkinson's disease**.

To produce the number of stem cells needed for this type of treatment, it's necessary to **clone embryos**.

Stem cells are collected at the **8-cell stage** when cells are **specialised**. At the 16-cell stage specialisation begins. It's possible to still use cells up to the 150-cell stage. However, they aren't as **effective**.

The Ethical Issue

There's an **issue** as to whether it's right to clone embryos and extract stem cells. The debate is about whether these embryos should be seen as people. One view is that if an embryo is produced for IVF but not implanted, it no longer has a future. So, it's acceptable to use with parental consent.

It's been suggested that embryos could be cloned from the patient's cells. This is the first stage in **reproductive cloning** (a new individual identical to the donor), which is illegal in the UK.

Governments make **laws** on issues. **Special advisory committees** explore the **ethics** of procedures such as cloning and stem cell use.

Key Words

Asexual reproduction • Clone • Ethics • Gene therapy • Stem cell

Module B1 Summary

Variation and Genetic Information

Variation = differences between individuals of the same species, due to **genetic** or **environmental** factors.

Genes…
- are sections of **DNA** (deoxyribonucleic acid) in **chromosomes**
- are located inside the **nucleus**
- carry the information needed for you to develop
- issue instructions to the cell to make **proteins**.

Alleles = different versions of a gene:
- **Dominant** – control a characteristic if present.
- **Recessive** – control a characteristic if it's present on both chromosomes.

HT **Proteins** inside a cell can be **structural** or **enzymes**.

Chromosomes

Chromosomes…
- are made of DNA
- normally come in pairs. (Both pairs have the same gene sequence.)

Human sex cells contain single chromosomes.

There are two sex chromosomes – X and Y:
- **XX** chromosomes = girl
- **XY** chromosomes = boy.

HT The sex of an individual is determined by a gene on the Y chromosome called the **sex-determining region Y** gene.

Genetic diagrams and **family trees** ➡ Used to identify how you inherit a characteristic.

Genetic Disorders

A fetus can be **genetically tested** for a **faulty allele** by **amniocentisis** testing and **chorionic villus** testing.

Embryo selection is…
- used to prevent babies having genetic disorders (IVF)
- controversial.

Disorder	Part of Body Affected	Cause
Huntington's	Central nervous system	Dominant allele
Cystic fibrosis	Cell membranes	Recessive allele

HT **Pre-implantation genetic diagnosis** – cells are tested for a specific genetic disorder.

Gene Therapy

Gene therapy ➤ **healthy genes** inserted into cells to treat a disease.

Gene therapy could be used as a **potential treatment** for genetic disorders.

Gene therapy raises **ethical questions** – people may see it as an **'unnatural'** procedure.

Clones

Asexual reproduction = single cell organisms **divide** to form two new individuals.

Bacteria and other **single-cell organisms** can reproduce asexually.

Clones = new individuals identical to the parent.

Clones can occur naturally to form **identical twins**.

HT **Animal clones** can be produced **artificially**.

Stem Cells

Most organisms are made of **specialised cells** with **different structures**.

Stem cells…
- are cells in the early stages of development that are not yet **specialised**
- have the potential to develop into **any type** of cell
- have the potential to **replace damaged** tissues.

There's an **issue** as to whether it's right or wrong to clone embryos and use stem cells.

Genetics and Ethics

Ethical questions (e.g. Is it right to interfere?) need to be addressed before genetic testing becomes common.

Special advisory committees advise the government which makes laws on the ethics of such procedures.

Decisions about ethical questions are normally based on what will **benefit** the **majority**.

There will always be people who **object** to a decision.

HT There is a danger that **storing genetic information** could be used to **discriminate**.

Governments may have the ability to test, but should they be allowed to?

There is a difference between what **can** be done and what **should** be done.

Module B1 Practice Questions

1 Circle the correct option in the following sentence:

A gene provides instructions to make **chromosomes / proteins / nuclei / cells**.

HT **2** What are the two types of protein formed inside cells?

a) ....

b) ....

3 Fill in the missing word to complete the sentence below:

Different versions of the same gene are called ....

4 Complete the genetic diagram below.

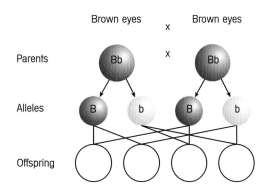

Brown eyes   x   Brown eyes

Parents   Bb   x   Bb

Alleles   B   b   B   b

Offspring

5 Niamh is growing yeast, a single-celled fungus, in an experiment. She adds a small sample of the yeast to a growth mixture. After a few days there's more yeast in the flask than she had to start with.

Use the words below to complete the following sentences.

asexual	X	sexual	Y	genetic
Z	environmental	chromosomes	nucleus	clones

a) The cells that make up Niamh's skin contain 23 pairs of ....

b) Yeast reproduces via .... reproduction.

c) All the yeast are genetically identical, therefore they are ....

d) The yeast don't look exactly the same. This is due to .... factors.

e) Niamh was produced by .... reproduction.

f) Niamh is female because she inherited an X chromosome from her father and a .... chromosome from her mother.

Module B1 Practice Questions

6 **a)** Which part of the body does Huntington's disorder affect?

....

b) Name two symptoms of...

i) Huntington's disorder ....

ii) Cystic fibrosis ....

7 There are two ways of removing cells so that a genetic test can be carried out on a fetus to see if it has a genetic disorder. Name them and circle the test which takes place at 8–10 weeks of pregnancy.

....

8 The table below is jumbled. Draw lines from each outcome to the correct test result and reality. One line has been drawn for you.

Outcome	Test Result	Reality
True positive	Fetus **has** the disorder	Fetus **does not** have the disorder
True negative	Fetus **has** the disorder	Fetus **has** the disorder
False positive	Fetus **does not** have the disorder	Fetus **has** the disorder
False negative	Fetus **does not** have the disorder	Fetus **does not** have the disorder

9 Fill in the missing words to complete the sentence below:

Bacteria and other .... organisms can .... by .... to form two new individuals.

10 Complete and label the diagram below to show how 'daughter' cells are formed.

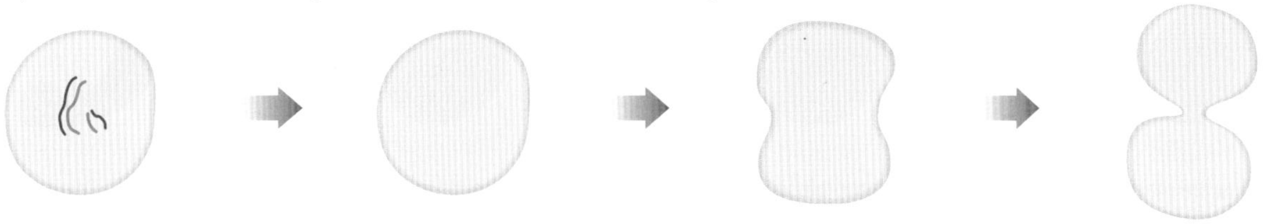

Parental cell with two pairs of chromosomes. → Each chromosome replicates itself. → .... → ....

Keeping Healthy

Infection

Infections are caused by harmful microorganisms:
- **Bacteria**, e.g. bubonic plague, TB and cystitis. Treated by antibiotics.

- **Fungi**, e.g. athlete's foot, thrush and ringworm. Treated by anti-fungal medicine and antibiotics.
- **Viruses**, e.g. Asian bird flu, common cold, HIV, measles and smallpox. Very difficult to treat.

The Body's Defence System

Microorganisms can be found on any surface and in the air we breathe.

The human body has a defence system of **physical** and **chemical** barriers which stop you getting ill:
- **Skin** forms a physical barrier.
- Chemicals in **sweat** and **tears**, and **hydrochloric acid** in the stomach, kill microorganisms.

The body provides ideal conditions for microorganisms to grow; it's **warm** with plenty of **nutrients** and **moisture**. Once in your body, harmful microorganisms reproduce very rapidly.

Symptoms of an illness only show when there's a significant amount of infection. The symptoms are caused by microorganisms damaging infected cells, e.g. bursting or producing harmful toxins.

The Immune Response

If microorganisms get into your body, the **immune system** is activated. Two types of **white blood cells** play a major role in this response.

One type of white blood cell is activated when you cut yourself:

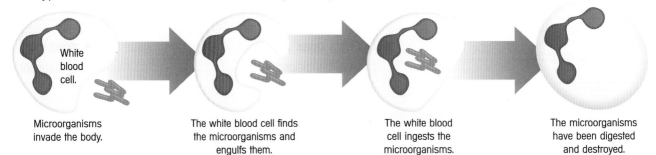

| Microorganisms invade the body. | The white blood cell finds the microorganisms and engulfs them. | The white blood cell ingests the microorganisms. | The microorganisms have been digested and destroyed. |

Another type of white blood cell makes **antibodies**:

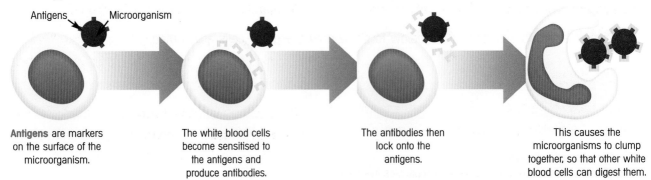

| **Antigens** are markers on the surface of the microorganism. | The white blood cells become sensitised to the antigens and produce antibodies. | The antibodies then lock onto the antigens. | This causes the microorganisms to clump together, so that other white blood cells can digest them. |

Specialisation of Antibodies

Different microorganisms cause different diseases. Microorganisms have **unique markers**, called **antigens**, on their surface. White blood cells produce antibodies specific to the marker they need to attack.

White blood cells 'remember' the antigens after infection and can produce antibodies quicker if the microorganism appears again. This is **natural immunity**.

Example – antibodies to fight TB will not fight cholera.

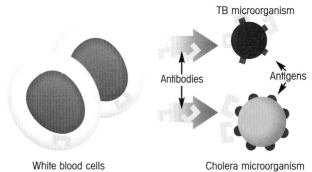

White blood cells

TB microorganism

Antibodies

Antigens

Cholera microorganism

Vaccination

A **vaccination** helps the body develop **immunity** and produce **specific** antibodies so microorganisms can be destroyed before they cause **infection**.

Vaccinations are never completely safe and can produce **side effects**. Most side effects are minor, e.g. mild fever or rash, but some people are affected more than others.

Extreme side effects like encephalitis (inflammation of the brain) are **rare**. The MMR vaccine has a 1 in 1 000 000 chance of encephalitis, but the risk of getting it from measles itself is much higher.

1 A weakened/dead strain of the microorganism is injected. Antigens on the modified microorganism's surface cause the white blood cells to produce specific antibodies.

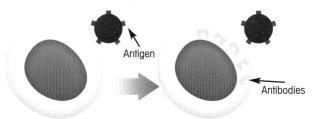

Antigen

Antibodies

2 The white blood cells that are capable of quickly producing the specific antibody remain in the bloodstream.

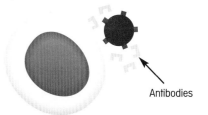

Antibodies

Mutating Viruses

Some vaccines have to be redeveloped regularly because viruses can **mutate** (change) to produce **new strains**. For example, flu vaccinations are **renewed every year** because new strains appear.

Key Words

Antibody • Antigen • Bacteria • Fungi • Immune system • Mutate • Natural immunity • Side effect • Virus

HT **HIV** (Human Immunodeficiency Virus) attacks the **immune system** and can lead to **AIDS** (Acquired Immune Deficiency Syndrome).

Infected people can die from illnesses like the common cold. HIV can be carried for years without being detected and can be passed on.

HIV is difficult to make a vaccine for. It **infects** the **white blood cells** that normally fight viruses. HIV can **mutate rapidly** and produce new strains.

Keeping Healthy

Choices

People can refuse to have a vaccination. But the more who say no, the greater the chance of a **disease outbreak** (epidemic) and the **faster** it will spread.

HT It's important to vaccinate as many people as possible to prevent epidemics like measles. If **more** than 95% of the population are vaccinated then the unvaccinated will be protected too, as the risk of

contact with an infected person is **small**. If the percentage drops **below** 95% then there's a greater chance of contact with infected people.

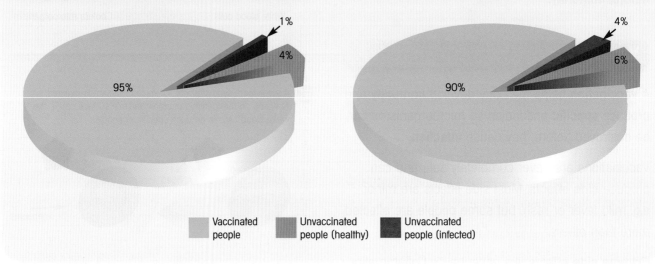

Vaccinated people	Unvaccinated people (healthy)	Unvaccinated people (infected)

Vaccination Policy

Health authorities have to develop a policy for each vaccination to **benefit the majority**. People hold different views so there will always be those who disagree.

HT The following **key factors** should be considered:
- How **high** is the **risk** of infection? Is the disease common in the UK?
- Who is **most at risk** e.g. the young, the elderly?
- Is the vaccination **safe**? Has it been tested for side effects?
- What is the **cost**? Can the Government afford to give free vaccines?

There's a difference between what **can** be done and what **should** be done.

For example, the government might have the ability to vaccinate everyone, but it can't force people to have a vaccination. People may refuse to have a vaccination for different reasons:
- It may conflict with religious / personal **beliefs**.
- Society gives us the right to **choose**.
- Some people may be more prone to side effects.

Different courses of action may be taken in different social and environmental contexts.

Antibiotics

Antibiotics are chemicals (drugs):
- They can kill **bacteria** and **fungi**.
- They can't kill **viruses** (so aren't prescribed for colds).

Resistance to Antibiotics

Over time, bacteria and fungi can become **resistant** to antibiotics.

HT **Random mutations** can occur in the genes of microorganisms:
- **New strains** develop.
- These are less affected by antibiotics so they can **reproduce** and **pass on** their resistance.

As varieties of bacteria and fungi become resistant, there are **fewer ways** to defeat them.

There's growing concern that microorganisms which are resistant to all drugs will develop (i.e. superbugs). In the UK, diseases such as MRSA (Methicillin Resistant Staphylococcus aureus) have a high degree of drug resistance.

To help prevent antibiotic resistance…
- doctors should only prescribe them when **completely necessary**
- patients should always **complete the course**.

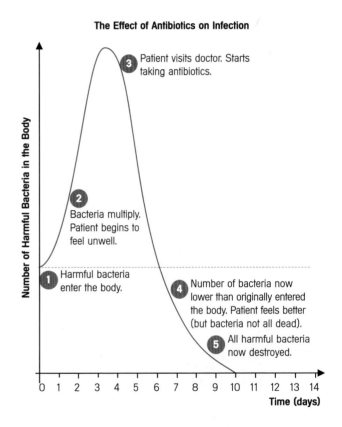

The Effect of Antibiotics on Infection

- ① Harmful bacteria enter the body.
- ② Bacteria multiply. Patient begins to feel unwell.
- ③ Patient visits doctor. Starts taking antibiotics.
- ④ Number of bacteria now lower than originally entered the body. Patient feels better (but bacteria not all dead).
- ⑤ All harmful bacteria now destroyed.

Number of Harmful Bacteria in the Body

Time (days): 0 1 2 3 4 5 6 7 8 9 10 11 12 13 14

Key Words

Antibiotic • Bacteria • Fungi • Virus

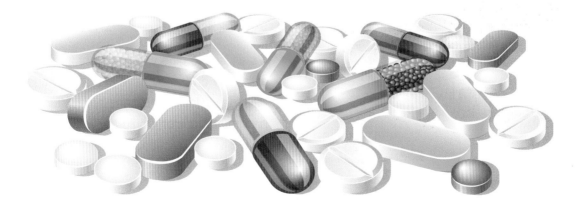

Keeping Healthy

Testing New Drugs

New drugs are tested for **safety** and **effectiveness** before they can be used. The methods used are often controversial.

Tests on Human Cells grown in the Laboratory	Tests on Animals
Advantages • Shows if drugs are effective. • Shows if drugs will damage cells. • No people or animals are harmed. **Disadvantages** • Doesn't show effects on whole organism. • Some say growing human cells is wrong.	**Advantages** • Shows if drugs are effective within body conditions. • Shows if drugs are safe for whole body. **Disadvantages** • Animals can suffer and die. • Animals may react differently to humans.

Clinical Trials

Clinical trials are carried out on…
• **healthy volunteers** to test for safety
• people with the illness to test for safety and effectiveness.

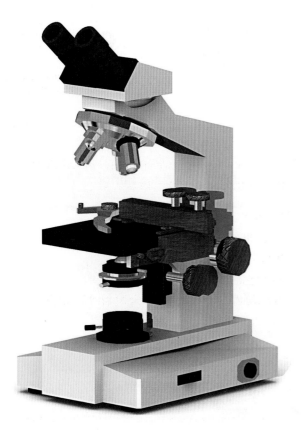

HT Clinical trials compare the effects of **new** and **old** drugs.

Blind trials – Patients **don't know** which drugs they're given but the doctor **does**. If the patient knows, they may give biased information. It's possible the doctor's body language may give clues.

Double-blind trials – Neither patient nor doctor know which drug is used. Results should be very accurate, due to removing bias. Sometimes it's impossible to keep what the drug is from the doctor, e.g. if the patient says the new drug has a different taste.

Placebos (dummy drugs) are occasionally used but create an ethical dilemma. They give **false hope**; the patient hopes the pill cures them, but the doctor knows it will not.

It's difficult to hide which patient is taking a placebo as a new drug may have certain obvious side effects, e.g. increased urine production. So, the patient and doctor would know if the patient had been given a placebo.

The Heart

The heart…
- pumps blood around the body in order to provide cells with **oxygen** and **nutrients**, and take away **waste**
- is made up of **muscle cells**, so it needs a blood supply to **function** properly.

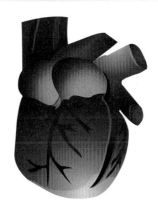

Arteries and Veins

The main blood vessels are **arteries** and **veins**. Their structure is related to their function.

Arteries carry blood away from the heart **towards** the organs. Substances from the blood can't pass through artery walls.

Veins carry blood from the organs **back** to the heart. Substances can't pass through the veins' walls.

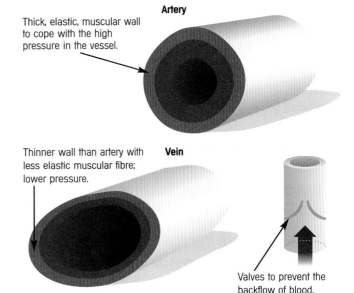

Artery

Thick, elastic, muscular wall to cope with the high pressure in the vessel.

Vein

Thinner wall than artery with less elastic muscular fibre; lower pressure.

Valves to prevent the backflow of blood.

Heart Disease

Heart disease…
- is a **structural** or **functional** abnormality which can lead to heart attack
- is usually caused by **lifestyle** and/or **genetic** factors. It's **not** caused by infection.

Lifestyle factors that can lead to heart disease include excessive alcohol, poor diet, smoking and stress.

A heart attack occurs when **fatty deposits** build up in blood vessels supplying the heart. Blood flow is restricted and muscle cells don't get enough oxygen and nutrients.

Heart disease is more common in the UK than in non-industrialised countries.

Precautions people can take include…
- regular exercise, e.g. 20 minutes brisk walking every day
- not smoking
- maintaining a healthy weight and reducing salt intake.

Key Words

Artery • Clinical trial • Placebo • Vein

Keeping Healthy

Epidemiological Studies

Epidemiological studies help identify **lifestyle factors** that lead to heart disease. These studies examine the **incidence** (number of cases) and **distribution** of heart disease in large populations.

Correlation

Scientists look at a large **cross-section** of cases to see if there's a **correlation** (link) between a factor and an outcome. For example, there is a correlation between a **high-fat diet** (factor) and **heart attacks** (outcome).

A large proportion of people who suffered heart attacks had a high-fat diet. But, not all people with a fatty diet had a heart attack. This suggests a fatty diet increases the chances of a heart attack, but doesn't always lead to one.

HT A correlation doesn't necessarily mean that the factor is a cause.

For example, a study could uncover a correlation between the number of kilograms someone is overweight and the amount of diet cola they consume. This doesn't mean diet cola causes obesity. In fact, they might drink diet cola because they're overweight.

Samples

Scientists look at a large sample of cases to see what is **typical** and what is **atypical** (unusual).

An individual case might be atypical. For example, someone who's smoked most of their life might live to 98 without getting lung cancer. If you looked at this case alone, you may think this proves that smoking helps you live longer!

To ensure a **fair test**, samples should be closely matched (e.g. similar diet and alcohol intake) so that only the factor being investigated varies.

HT Data can be used to argue whether or not a factor increases the chance of an outcome and to make predictions.

For example, the graph shows there's a negative correlation between the number of alcoholic drinks consumed and a person's dexterity (ability to move hands easily). As X increases, Y decreases. This means that given a value for X, it's possible to make a prediction of the value of Y.

Even if data supports a correlation, scientists may still reject it. It's only likely to be accepted if they can find a **plausible** (likely) explanation for how that factor can bring about the outcome.

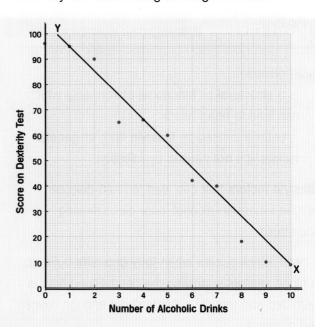

The Peer Review Process

Scientists follow procedures when conducting research like epidemiological studies to ensure their findings are reliable:

1. **Epidemiological study** – the scientist may discover a correlation and makes a **hypothesis**, e.g. that factor X increases the chance of outcome Y.
2. **Further investigation** – they conduct further experiments to gather data to test the hypothesis.
3. **Report findings** – the scientist writes a paper detailing the hypothesis, how the experiment was carried out, the results, and the conclusion (whether the data supports the hypothesis).
4. **Peer review** – peers (other scientists who work in that field) check the findings for faults and may repeat the experiments.
5. **Findings released** – if it's decided the research was correct and the conclusions are accurate, the findings are published or presented.
6. **Feedback** – all scientists can then **evaluate** it. It may lead to **further advances** or could be **challenged** – someone may see a new problem.

Reliability and Accuracy

The **peer review** process is very important. The more scientists that **evaluate** the findings, the more likely it is that **errors** or problems will be spotted, and the more **reliable** the results may be.

Sometimes preliminary results that haven't been fully reviewed by other scientists are leaked. These aren't reliable and may turn out to be inaccurate or wrong. Inaccurate information can cause problems, e.g. it can cause false hope or panic.

(HT) Unfortunately, a small minority of scientists make claims that **aren't true**. They might do this to improve their reputation or for funding.

If a new claim is reliable, other scientists should get the same results. If this isn't possible, the claim will not be trusted. Likewise, if a scientist refuses to show evidence (e.g. details of experiments and data), their findings must be taken as being **unreliable**.

Key Words

Epidemiological study • Peer review

Module B2 Summary

The Body's Defence System

Infections are caused by...
- **bacteria**
- **fungi**
- **viruses**.

The human body has a **defence system** of **physical** and **chemical barriers**.

Symptoms of an illness only show when there's a **significant** amount of infection.

Two types of **white blood cell** are part of the **immune system's response**:
- One type **engulfs** and **digests** microorganisms.
- Another type makes **antibodies**.

Antigens = unique markers on microorganisms.
White blood cells remember antigens to produce antibodies quicker.

Vaccination

Vaccination...
- helps the body develop **immunity** and produce **specific antibodies**
- can have **side effects**.

Some vaccines need to be developed regularly because viruses can **mutate**.

(HT) **HIV**...
- is difficult to make a vaccine for
- infects the white blood cells.

People can choose not to have a vaccination.

It's important to vaccinate as many people as possible to prevent **epidemics** and **reduce the risk** of becoming infected. **Health authorities** develop **policies** to benefit the **majority**.

(HT) The government may have the ability to vaccinate everyone, but it can't force people.

Different courses of action may be taken in different social and environmental contexts.

Antibiotics

Antibiotics are **chemicals** which kill **bacteria** and **fungi**. They **can't** kill **viruses**.

Bacteria and fungi can become **resistant** to antibiotics.

(HT) **Random gene mutations** occur in the microorganism ➡ **New strains** develop ➡ These are less affected by the drug and pass this resistance on.

Doctors should only prescribe antibiotics when **completely necessary**. Patients should **always complete the course**.

Testing New Drugs

New drugs are tested for **safety** and **effectiveness**. Methods can be controversial (e.g. testing on animals).

Clinical trials are carried out on healthy volunteers and people with the illness.

(HT) Clinical trials compare the effects of new and old drugs:
- **Blind Trials.**
- **Double-Blind Trials.**

Dummy drugs called **placebos** can be used. These can give false hope so create an ethical dilemma.

The Heart, Arteries and Veins

The **heart**…
- pumps blood to provide cells with **oxygen** and **nutrients** and take away **waste**
- is made up of muscle cells.

The main blood vessels are…
- **arteries**
- **veins**.

Heart disease is…
- a **structural** or **functional** abnormality which can lead to heart attack
- is usually caused by **lifestyle** (e.g. diet) and / or **genetic factors**.

Scientific Studies

Scientists look at a **large sample** to look for a **correlation** between a **factor** and an **outcome**.

Samples are closely matched to ensure a **fair test**.

(HT) A correlation doesn't always mean that the factor is a cause.

Data can be used to argue whether or not a factor increases the chance of an outcome and make predictions.

Peer Reviews

Peer Review process = other scientists check the results for errors to make sure the results are reliable.

(HT) A minority of scientists make claims that **aren't true**.

Findings must be taken as **unreliable** if a scientist **refuses** to show their evidence.

Module B2 Practice Questions

1 Name the three groups of disease-causing microorganisms.

a) _____ b) _____ c) _____

2 Bacteria can grow very rapidly. They can only do so if the correct conditions are present. Circle the three best factors for bacterial growth.

Warmth   **Safety**   **Humidity**   **Food**   **Attractiveness**

3 The body has a number of physical and chemical barriers to infection by microorganisms.
Fill in the labels on the diagram below to show these barriers.

a) _____

b) _____

c) _____

d) _____

4 **A, B, C** and **D** describe the four stages that take place when white blood cells attack a foreign microorganism. Put them in the correct order using numbers **1–4**.

A Microorganisms are ingested by the white blood cell. ◯

B Microorganisms are detected by the body. ◯

C Microorganisms are completely digested and destroyed. ◯

D White blood cell surrounds the microorganism. ◯

5 Label the diagram below which shows how the body fights infection.

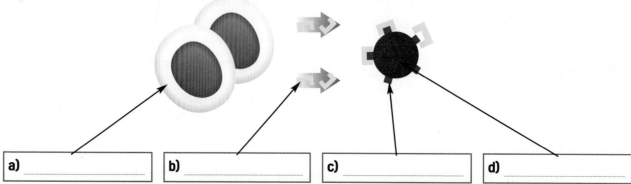

a) _____ b) _____ c) _____ d) _____

6 Vaccines prevent disease. What is contained in a vaccine? Tick the correct option.

A Antibiotics ⬭

B A weakened or dead strain of the disease-causing microorganism ⬭

C An active strain of the disease-causing microorganism ⬭

D Antibodies ⬭

7 a) Why can't vaccines ever be completely safe?

....

b) Why do new vaccines have to be developed regularly for diseases such as Flu?

....

HT **8** Which of the following statements about HIV are true? Tick the three correct options.

A HIV mutates at a high rate in the body. ⬭

B HIV mutates at a slow rate in the body. ⬭

C HIV attacks the immune system. ⬭

D New HIV strains are unaffected by a vaccine. ⬭

E Vaccines destroy new HIV strains. ⬭

F HIV improves the immune system. ⬭

9 Why is it important to finish a course of antibiotics?

....

....

10 Fill in the missing words to complete the sentences below:

The main blood vessels are .... and .... Heart attacks occur

when .... deposits build up in .... supplying the heart.

11 Scientists carry out research following certain procedures. Place the numbers **1–6** in the boxes to put the following stages in the correct order.

A Peer Review. ⬭

B Report Findings. ⬭

C Epidemiological Study. ⬭

D Feedback. ⬭

E Further Investigation. ⬭

F Release findings. ⬭

Life on Earth

Life on Earth

Life on Earth began about **3500 million** years ago.

During that time there has been a large number of species living on Earth, many of which are now **extinct**.

A species is a group of organisms which can freely breed with each other to produce fertile offspring.

The very first living things developed from **simple molecules** that could **copy** or **replicate** themselves.

It's not known whether these molecules…

- were produced by conditions on Earth at the time (harsh surface conditions, or in deep sea vents), or

- arrived on Earth from an external source, e.g. a comet hitting Earth.

Experiments have simulated the harsh conditions on Earth millions of years ago, which led to **simple organic molecules** developing.

There's evidence of simple organic molecules existing in gas clouds in space and in comets.

Key Words

Common ancestor • DNA • Evolution • Fossil • Natural selection

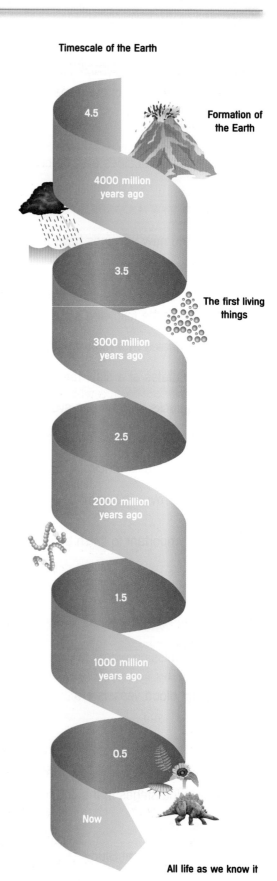

Timescale of the Earth

4.5 — Formation of the Earth

4000 million years ago

3.5 — The first living things

3000 million years ago

2.5

2000 million years ago

1.5

1000 million years ago

0.5

Now

All life as we know it

The Beginning of Life

Evidence suggests that all existing organisms share certain traits, including **cellular structure** and the **genetic** code, DNA. This would mean that all existing organisms share a common ancestor and evolved from very simple living things. Two sources of evidence support this: the fossil record and DNA evidence.

The Fossil Record

Fossil evidence supports the common ancestor theory and shows the history of species and the evolutionary changes over millions of years.

Fossils can be formed from the…
- hard parts of organisms that don't decay easily
- parts of animals and plants which haven't decayed because one or more of the conditions needed for decay were absent, e.g. oxygen or moisture
- soft parts of organisms which can be replaced by minerals as they decay. This can preserve traces of footprints or burrows.

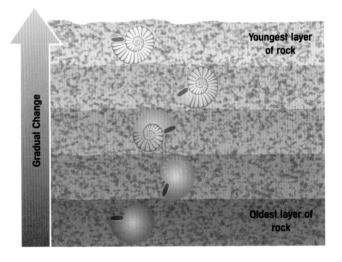

Evolution of Ammonites

Gradual Change

Youngest layer of rock

Oldest layer of rock

DNA Evidence

DNA evidence also supports the common ancestor theory. Analysing DNA of both living organisms and fossils shows the similarities and the differences.

This can be used to fill gaps in the **fossil record**. The more shared genes organisms have, the more closely related they are.

Comparing **gene sequences** reveals that the DNA of some organisms is very similar to organisms that seem very different.

For example, human DNA shares 98.8% of chimpanzee DNA, our nearest genetic relative. A mouse, which appears very dissimilar from humans, shares 85% of chimpanzee DNA.

Evolution by natural selection made life as it is today. If conditions on Earth had been different, then the results could have been very different.

Mouse   Chimpanzee   Human

Life on Earth

Evolution by Natural Selection

Evolution…
- is the slow, continual change over generations
- may result in a new species which is **better adapted** to its environment
- occurs due to natural selection, when individuals have characteristics which improve their chances of survival.

Four key points about natural selection:
1. Individuals show **variation**, i.e. differences due to their genes.
2. There's competition for food and mates. Also, disease and predators keep population sizes constant in spite of many offspring.
3. Those better adapted are more likely to survive and reproduce whilst others die out. This is 'survival of the fittest'.
4. Survivors pass on genes to their offspring, resulting in an improved organism evolving over generations.

Natural selection relies on variation caused by the environment and genes. However, only a **genetic variation** can be passed on. For example, if you lost a finger, this characteristic wouldn't be passed on. This is environmental variation.

Increased competition has seen grey squirrels outnumber red squirrels.

(HT) Peppered Moths are naturally pale and speckled, so are well camouflaged against silver birch trees.

However, during the Industrial Revolution, air pollution discoloured the trees with soot and natural selection led to a **new variety** of Peppered Moth:
1. **Variation** – some moths were naturally darker due to their genes.
2. **Competition** – darker-coloured and paler moths had to compete for food.
3. **Better adapted** – darker moths were better camouflaged against the blackened trees and buildings. Paler moths were seen by birds and were eaten.
4. **Passing on genes** – darker moths were more likely to survive and breed, passing on their genes for darker pigmentation.

The Clean Air Act reduced air pollution which meant more silver birch trees stayed 'silver'. This gave the pale variety an advantage so numbers began to grow again. Today, the presence of the pale variety is regarded as a clean air marker.

Peppered Moth

Dark Peppered Moth

Key Words

Competition • Environmental variation • Evolution • Mutation • Natural selection • Selective breeding • Survival of the fittest

HT Gene Mutation

A change in a gene is a mutation. Occasionally, mutations can alter the properties of a **protein** and can influence the **development** of an organism.

If this happens in a **sex cell** then the mutated gene can be passed on to the offspring, which may show **new characteristics**.

A new species can be produced through the combined effects of **mutations, environmental changes** and **natural selection**.

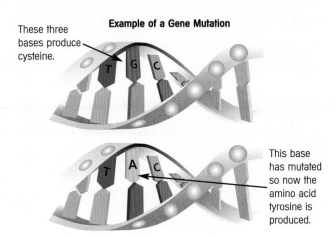

Example of a Gene Mutation

These three bases produce cysteine.

This base has mutated so now the amino acid tyrosine is produced.

Selective Breeding

Selective breeding is when animals with certain traits are mated to produce offspring with certain desirable characteristics. Selective breeding can produce two outcomes:

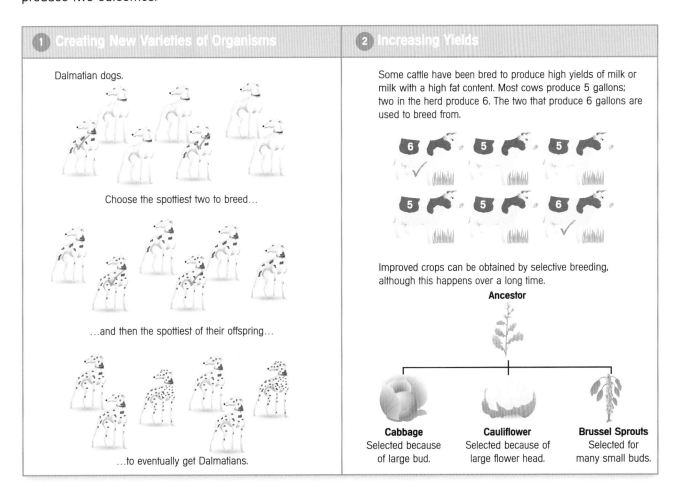

1 Creating New Varieties of Organisms

Dalmatian dogs.

Choose the spottiest two to breed...

...and then the spottiest of their offspring...

...to eventually get Dalmatians.

2 Increasing Yields

Some cattle have been bred to produce high yields of milk or milk with a high fat content. Most cows produce 5 gallons; two in the herd produce 6. The two that produce 6 gallons are used to breed from.

Improved crops can be obtained by selective breeding, although this happens over a long time.

Ancestor

Cabbage
Selected because of large bud.

Cauliflower
Selected because of large flower head.

Brussel Sprouts
Selected for many small buds.

Life on Earth

The Evolution of Humans

It's thought that apes and humans share a common ancestor. The investigation of **fossil records** was the basis of this idea.

The Hominid family, i.e. humans, gorillas and orangutans, **branched** during evolution and several Homo species developed.

Homo sapiens is now the only living species of its type and other Homo species are now **extinct**.

Natural selection is most likely to have caused hominids' brain size to **increase** over time because...
- there's a rough correlation between brain size and intelligence
- large brains would give individuals an advantage, making them more likely to survive.

It was originally thought that brain size would have increased before hominids began walking upright. However, fossil evidence suggests that walking upright came first.

This shows the role of observations and data in establishing the **reliability** of an explanation.

If new observations or data agree with a theory it increases confidence in the explanation.

(HT) However, it doesn't necessarily prove that the theory is correct.

If new observations or data disagree, it indicates that either the observations or data are wrong, or the theory is wrong.

(HT) This may, therefore, decrease our confidence in the explanation.

When this happens, further investigations are carried out to establish where the error lies. If the new observations or data prove reliable, then the theory will be revised. This is how scientific explanations change over time.

Members of the Homo Group

Common Ancestor
Homo habilis
(evidence exists they were the earliest ancestor, using simple tools)

Common Ancestor
Homo erectus
(had large brains and may have used fire to cook)

Cousin
Homo neanderthalensis
(close cousin of *Homo sapiens*)

Cousin
Homo sapiens
(present-day humans)

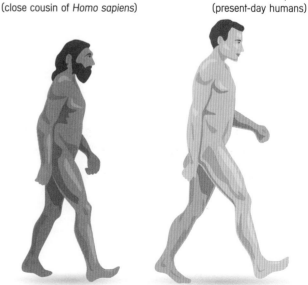

Origins of Life

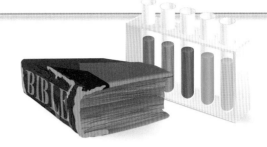

How life on Earth began has long been debated:
- Religions say God, or a creator, created all life.
- Scientists have testable theories that try to explain similarities between organisms.

Inheritance of Acquired Characteristics

Jean-Baptiste Lamarck devised the theory that an animal evolved over its lifetime; the more an animal used part of its body, the more it would adapt. For example, a giraffe stretching for leaves would develop a long neck.

A scientist called Weismann cast doubt on Lamarck's theory. He cut the tails off mice and bred them. The mice produced offspring with tails, conflicting with Lamarck's explanation.

However, Lamarck said Weismann's experiment was deliberate mutation and that only situations where the animal desired change were valid.

Lamarck used **imagination** and **creativity** to develop his explanation, but Weismann's evidence led to the **rejection** of Lamarck's theory.

HT Scientific explanations are not abandoned when conflicting data is found because…
- new data may be incorrect
- explanations based on new data can run into problems
- many scientists will have based work on the existing explanation and will stick with it.

A new explanation is only likely to replace another once it's proven to be reliable.

Evolution by Natural Selection

In the 1830s Charles Darwin created a testable theory of evolution, studying different types of finch on the Galapagos Islands.

Darwin made four important observations for his theory: **variety**, **competition**, **survival of the fittest**, and **passing on desirable characteristics**.

HT Darwin linked these observations and deduced that the **best-adapted** organisms would **survive** and **reproduce**. This was the basis of his theory of **'Evolution by Natural Selection'**.

Scientists can't ever be certain how life began; evidence is scarce and theories are based on the evidence available at the time. New discoveries are still being made and developing our scientific knowledge.

Key Words

Common ancestor • Hominid •
Theory of Evolution

Life on Earth

The Extinction of Species

Species have become extinct over time, e.g. the dodo. The usual cause is a species' inability to adapt to change in the form of...

- **increased competition**
- new **predators**
- change in the **environment**
- new **diseases**.

Mass extinctions...

- are when many species disappear in a relatively short time
- occur when environmental change happens so quickly that animals and plants can't adapt fast enough.

Human activity has been responsible for the extinction of some species. For example...

- the introduction of new predators or competition, e.g. mitten crabs travelled in ships to the UK, where they eat native species of crab
- industrial activities causing global warming
- deforestation clears areas, increases carbon dioxide levels and alters the carbon cycle.

The Dodo

Extinctions Caused Directly by Man

The **Great Auk** (a sea bird)...

- only laid one egg a year and couldn't fly, so was vulnerable
- was hunted for food and its down. The last pair was killed in 1844.

The **smallpox** virus...

- was eradicated deliberately by man by mass vaccination
- was declared extinct in 1980. The only examples are stored in two laboratories.

Extinctions Caused Indirectly by Man

The **Rodrigues pigeon**...

- was native to Rodrigues Island in the Indian Ocean
- became extinct when ships visiting the island accidently introduced rats, which preyed on the birds.

The **Gould's Mouse**...

- disappeared rapidly after Europeans settled in Australia – they were affected by changes to their habitat
- was thought to have been hunted by cats and killed by diseases from rats and mice (which were introduced by man).

Maintaining Biodiversity

Every time a species becomes extinct, information stored in its genetic code is **lost**.

Projects like the Kew Gardens Millennium Seed Bank Project prevent this by collecting and storing seeds from all over the world.

Extinctions mean **less variety** on Earth. Without variety people would start to run out of food crops and medicines. Many medicines are developed from plants or animals. There are potentially many medicines in areas like the Amazon rainforest – an area rapidly undergoing deforestation.

By understanding how our actions can impact on biodiversity, scientists hope to discover ways to use the Earth's resources in a sustainable way.

Food Chains

Organisms don't live in isolation. Different species of animals or plants compete for resources in the same habitat.

Food chains can show the feeding relationships between organisms. When animals eat plants or other animals, energy is passed up the food chain.

Animals are dependent upon each other and their environment for survival.

For example, if rabbits became extinct, then the stoat and the fox may be at risk. Their numbers may then be reduced as competition for food increased.

Food Webs

Food webs...
- show how all the food chains in a habitat are **inter-related**
- can be complicated as many animals have **varied** diets.

Environmental changes can alter the food web. For example, less rain could reduce the amount of lettuces and cause reductions in slug numbers.

If the changes are too great, organisms will die before they can reproduce, eventually becoming extinct.

Food Web

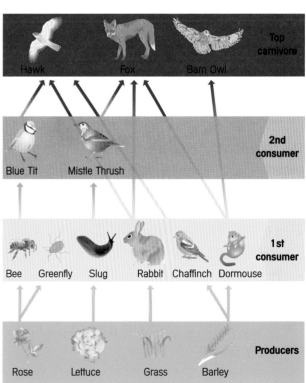

Key Words

Extinct • Biodiversity • Sustainable • Food chain • Food web

Life on Earth

Communication Systems

The evolution of **multi-cellular** organisms eventually led to the development of nervous and hormonal **communication systems**.

Nerve impulses are **electrical signals**. They are **rapid** and **short-lived**.

Hormone signals are **chemical** messages in the blood. They are **slow-acting** and **longer-lasting** than nerve impulses.

Hormones regulate the functions of many organs and cells.

HT The maintenance of a constant internal body environment (temperature, etc.) is called **homeostasis.**

The body uses nervous signals and hormonal signals to ensure the systems are stable.

Hormones and Human Fertility

Human fertility is an example of hormone communication. A woman produces hormones that cause an egg to mature and be released:
1. Follicle stimulating hormone (FSH) from the **pituitary gland** causes the ovaries to produce oestrogen and an egg to mature. There are changes in the thickness of the lining of the womb.
2. Oestrogen, produced in the ovaries, inhibits the production of FSH and causes the production of luteinising hormone (LH).
3. LH, also from the pituitary gland, stimulates the release of an egg in the middle of the menstrual cycle.

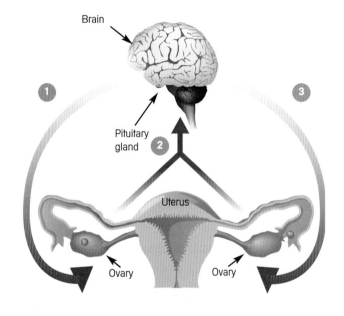

Hormones and Insulin

The body's use of **insulin** is an example of hormone communication. The pancreas produces insulin. Its level in the blood is governed by the amount of **glucose** in the blood:
- If the glucose concentration increases, insulin is released into the bloodstream.
- The insulin causes cells to take in the glucose.
- Any additional glucose is stored as glycogen.

The transportation of glucose is governed by the circulatory system.

The Central Nervous System

The nervous system is based around…

- **sensor** (receptor) cells that detect stimuli
- **effector** cells that respond to the stimuli.

Neurons (**nerve cells**) connect the sensor cells (e.g. in the eyes, ears and skin) and effector cells (e.g. muscles, glands) together. Neurons are specially adapted cells that carry an electrical signal impulse.

The coordination of the nervous system in humans, and other vertebrates, is carried out by the **central nervous system**, which consists of the spinal cord and brain.

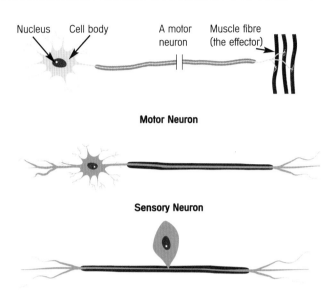

Motor Neuron

Sensory Neuron

Involuntary Responses to Stimuli

Removing your hand from a pin is an example of an **involuntary or reflex nervous action**.

1. A receptor is stimulated by the drawing pin, which is the **stimulus**.
2. This causes **impulses** to pass along a **sensory neuron** into the **spinal cord**.
3. The sensory neuron **synapses** (communicates) with a **relay neuron**, bypassing the brain.
4. The relay neuron synapses with a **motor neuron**, sending impulses down it.
5. These impulses reach the **effectors** (muscles), causing them to contract and remove the hand in response to the sharp drawing pin.

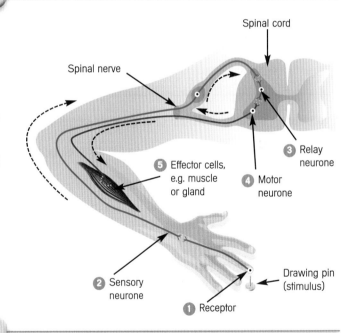

Voluntary Responses to Stimuli

Turning down loud music is an example of a **voluntary nervous reaction**.

Sound-sensitive receptors detect loud music. Sensory neurones pass an electrical signal to the central nervous system where the information is processed.

A response, in the form of another electrical signal, is sent by the motor neuron to the effector cells in the muscles in the arms and fingers.

The arm and finger muscles respond by covering the ears to block the sound and then turning the volume down.

Key Words

Central nervous system • Effector • Hormone • Neuron • Sensor • Stimulus

Module B3 Summary

Life on Earth

Life on Earth began about **3500 million years ago**.

The very first living things developed from **simple molecules** that could **replicate** themselves.

It's not known whether the molecules were produced on Earth or from an **external source**.

Common Ancestors

Evidence suggests all existing organisms…
- have a **common ancestor**
- share **cellular structure** and **genetic code**.

DNA and Fossil Evidence

The common ancestor theory is supported by…
- **fossil evidence** – shows the **evolutionary changes** over millions of years
- **DNA evidence** – shows the **similarities** between organisms.

The more shared genes organisms have, the more **closely related** they are.

Evolution by Natural Selection

Evolution = a slow, continual change over generations.

Evolution by **natural selection** made life as it is today. If conditions had been different then the results could have been **very different**.

In natural selection…
- individuals show **variation**
- there's **competition** for food and mates
- those **better adapted** will survive – **'Survival of the fittest'**
- survivors **pass on** their genes

Natural selection relies on variation caused by the **environment** and **genes**.

Only **genetic variations** can be passed on. **Environmental variations** aren't passed on.

HT Gene Mutation

A change in a gene is a **mutation**.

Mutations can **alter the properties** of a protein and **influence the development** of an organism.

A **new species** can be produced through the combined effects of **mutations, environmental changes** and **natural selection**.

The Evolution of Humans

The **Hominid** family **branched** during evolution ➡ Several Homo species developed.

Homo sapiens is now the only living species of its type.

Hominids' brain size would have **increased** over time, making them more likely to survive. There's a rough **correlation** between brain size and intelligence.

Fossil evidence suggests that walking upright came before brain size increased.

The Extinction of Species

Species have become **extinct** over time.

Extinctions are usually caused by an inability to adapt to…
* increased **competition**
* new **predators**
* **environmental changes**
* **new diseases**.

Mass extinctions are when many species disappear quickly because organisms can't adapt fast enough.

Human activity has been responsible for the extinction of some species and can affect **biodiversity – less variety** on Earth.

Food chains and **food webs** can show how organisms' diets in a habitat are **inter-related**.

Nerves and Hormones

Nerve impulses are **electrical, rapid** and **short-lived**.

Hormone signals are **chemical, slow** and **longer-lasting**.

(HT) The maintenance of a constant internal body environment is called **homeostasis**.

The **nervous system** is based around **sensors** and **receptors**. These are connected by specially-adapted cells called **neurons** that carry **electrical signals**.

The **central nervous system** consists of the **spinal cord** and **brain**.

Scientific Explanation

Observations and data are important to reach a reliable explanation.

Investigations are carried out to test a theory. If the results disagree, further investigations try to establish where the error lies.

Module B3 Practice Questions

1 How long ago is it thought that life first began on Earth?

....

2 Give two pieces of evidence to support the suggestion that all existing organisms have a common ancestor.

a) ....

b) ....

3 **a)** Fill in the missing words to complete the sentences below:

Fossils show the .... of species and the .... changes

over millions of years.

b) Analysing .... can be used to fill gaps in the fossil record.

c) The more shared .... organisms have, the more closely

.... they are.

4 Evolution occurs through natural selection. Which of the following factors are necessary for natural selection to occur? Tick the four correct options.

A Variation ◯	**B** Attractive colours ◯	
C Better adapted ◯	**D** Pass on genes ◯	
E Competition ◯	**F** Similarities ◯	
G Good communication ◯	**H** High DNA content ◯	

5 What is environmental variation? Give an example of this.

....

....

....

6 Circle the correct options in the following sentence:

Selective breeding is when animals and plants with certain traits are deliberately **separated / mutated / mated / evolved** to provide offspring with desirable **organisms / characteristics / cells / structures**.

7 Give three reasons why a species may become extinct.

a) ....

b) ....

c) ....

8 Maintaining biodiversity is important. Circle the correct options in the following sentence:

Biodiversity is important because without **competition / characteristics / variety / evolution** we would run out of food, medicines and **variety / characteristics / resources / competition**.

9 Construct a food chain using **Greenfly**, **Blackbird**, **Oak tree** and **Ladybird**. Write the name of each organism in the correct box below.

....	....	....	....

10 What are the two systems of sending messages in the body?

a) ....

b) ....

11 The diagram below shows the body's involuntary response to stimuli. Match statements **A–E** with the labels **1–5** on the diagram. Enter the appropriate number in the boxes provided.

A Impulses pass along a sensory neuron into the spinal cord. ◯

B The muscles contract in response to pain. ◯

C A receptor is stimulated. ◯

D The sensory neuron synapses with a relay neurone, bypassing the brain. ◯

E The relay neuron synapses with a motor neuron, sending impulses down it. ◯

Homeostasis

Homeostasis

Homeostasis is the maintenance of a constant internal environment. It's achieved by…

- balancing bodily inputs and outputs
- removing waste products.

Your body has **automatic control systems** which maintain steady levels of…

- **temperature**
- **water** (**hydration**).

These factors enable your cells to function properly.

The failure of homeostasis results in death.

Factors Affecting Homeostasis

Homeostasis can be affected by…

- exercise
- the temperature of your surroundings.

When you do strenuous exercise, your body temperature increases and you lose water through sweat. Your body needs to get rid of the excess heat and replace the lost water so that your systems will continue to work correctly.

In **hot climates** your body temperature can rise and water levels can drop.

In **cold climates** your body loses heat and this can lead to **hypothermia**.

HT Homeostasis can also be affected by changes in…
- **blood oxygen levels**
- **salt levels.**

Scuba divers use equipment to make sure that their blood oxygen is kept at the correct level. They wear wetsuits to prevent their bodies from cooling down too much.

Mountain climbers wear breathing apparatus to make sure that their blood oxygen is kept at the correct level.

Key Words

Effector • Homeostasis • Hypothermia • Incubator • Receptor

Artificial Homeostasis

Artificial homeostasis is needed when the body's control systems don't work correctly.

For example, an **incubator** helps a premature baby to survive by controlling its temperature and oxygen levels.

Artificial systems and body systems both have…
- **receptors** (sensors) to detect stimuli
- **processing centres** to receive information and coordinate responses
- **effectors** which automatically produce the response.

HT Negative Feedback

Negative feedback works to maintain a **steady state**. When the conditions rise above / fall beneath a set level, the response is to reverse the direction of change.

When the temperature inside an incubator **exceeds** a set level, the following happens:
1. Temperature rise is detected by a sensor (**receptor**).
2. The **processing centre** in the computer responds by sending a signal to the heater.
3. The heater (**effector**) turns off.

The temperature inside the incubator may then **drop below** a set level and the following happens:
1. Fall in temperature is detected by a sensor (**receptor**).
2. The **processing centre** in the computer responds by sending a signal to the heater.
3. The heater (**effector**) turns on.

Conditions in the body change from set point → Change detected → Corrective response activated → Conditions return to set point → Corrective response switched off

Antagonistic Effectors

In many systems there are effectors that act **antagonistically** (i.e. as opposites) to one another.

For example, one effector is responsible for increasing temperature whilst another is responsible for decreasing the temperature.

This method of control is far more sensitive and accurate.

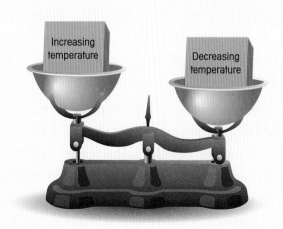

Homeostasis

Body Temperature

Energy loss and **energy gain** from your body need to be balanced so that your body temperature remains **constant**.

The temperature of your body's extremities tends to be cooler than your core body temperature. Energy is transferred from the **blood** to the **tissues** when it reaches the cooler parts.

Controlling body temperature requires...

- **temperature receptors in the skin** to detect the external temperature
- **temperature receptors in the brain** to measure the temperature of the blood
- **the brain** which acts as a processing centre, to receive information from the temperature receptors, responding by triggering the **effectors**
- effectors (sweat glands and muscles) to carry out the automatic response.

If your body temperature is **too high**, heat needs to be transferred to the environment. This is done by **sweating**, since **evaporation** from the skin requires heat energy from the body.

If your body temperature is **too low**, your body will start to **shiver**. Shivering is the rapid **contraction** and release of muscles. These contractions require energy from increased **respiration**, and heat is released as a by-product, warming surrounding tissue.

(HT) Vasodilation and Vasoconstriction

Blood temperature is monitored by a centre in your brain called the hypothalamus.

In **hot conditions**, blood vessels in the skin **dilate**, allowing more blood to flow through the skin capillaries. This means that more heat is lost from the surface of the skin by radiation. This is called vasodilation.

In **cold conditions**, blood vessels in the skin **constrict**, reducing the amount of blood that flows through the skin capillaries. This means that less heat is lost from the surface of the skin by radiation. This is called vasoconstriction.

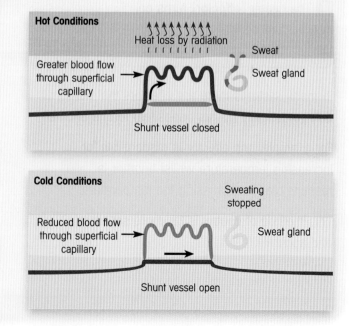

Heat Stroke

Heat stroke is an **uncontrolled** increase in your body temperature.

Increased sweating due to very hot temperatures can lead to **dehydration**. Dehydration stops sweating from occurring which leads to the core body temperature increasing even further.

If your body isn't cooled down, the normal systems for controlling body temperature break down and this results in death.

Causes of heat stroke include…
- exercising in very warm conditions
- very high humidity
- dehydration.

Symptoms of heat stroke are…
- confusion
- red/dry skin
- low blood pressure
- convulsions
- fainting
- rapid heartbeat.

Initially, you can treat heat stroke by…
- removing clothes and bathing in cool water
- cooling body using wet towels
- using a fan
- putting ice packs on the neck, head and groin
- elevating (raising) the legs.

Hypothermia

Hypothermia occurs when your body is exposed to **low temperatures** for a long period of time. Your body can't replace heat as fast as it's being lost and, if untreated, this can lead to death.

The common cause of hypothermia is when your **core body temperature** falls below **35°C**.

Symptoms of hypothermia are…
- grey skin colour
- amnesia (memory loss)
- shivering
- slurred speech
- confusion
- loss of coordination
- cold skin.

Initially, you can treat hypothermia by…
- raising the core body temperature
- insulating the body (particularly the armpits, head and groin)
- drinking warm drinks, but not alcohol.

N.B. You shouldn't rub or massage the skin – this brings blood to the surface, causing even more heat to be lost.

Key Words

Effector • Hypothalamus • **Hypothermia** • **Receptor** • Vasoconstriction • Vasodilation

Homeostasis

Water Balance

Water is **input** (gained) from…
- food and drinks
- respiration.

Water is **output** (lost) through…
- sweating
- breathing
- excretion of faeces and urine.

Your body has to **balance** these different inputs and outputs to ensure that there's enough water inside cells for cell activity to take place.

The Kidneys

Your kidneys filter your blood to remove **urea** (waste) and to balance levels of other chemicals (including water) transported in the blood plasma. They achieve this by…
- filtering small molecules from your blood to form urine (water, salt and urea)
- reabsorbing all the sugar
- reabsorbing as much salt as your body needs
- reabsorbing as much water as your body needs
- excreting remaining urine, stored in your **bladder**.

Right kidney

Left kidney

Bladder

Regulating Water Levels

Your kidneys balance the water level in your body:
- When the water level is **too high**, your kidneys reabsorb less water and a **large amount of dilute urine** is produced.
- When the water level is **too low**, your kidneys reabsorb more water and a **small amount of concentrated urine** is produced.

The amount of water that needs to reabsorbed into the blood plasma depends on…
- the external temperature
- the amount of exercise taken
- the fluid intake.

When **salt levels** increase, your body removes any excess salt by producing dilute urine. This means you need to intake more fluids to maintain a balanced water level.

Alcohol causes a large amount of dilute urine to be produced. This can lead to **dehydration**.

Ecstasy causes a small amount of concentrated urine to be produced.

Key Words

Anti-diuretic hormone • Hypothalamus • Pituitary gland • **Urea**

⒣ Anti-Diuretic Hormone

The concentration of urine is controlled by a hormone called anti-diuretic hormone (**ADH**), which is released into your blood via the pituitary gland.

Controlling water balance is an example of **negative feedback**.

When your blood water level becomes **too high** (i.e. there's too much water) the following happens:

❶ Receptors in your hypothalamus detect a decrease in salt concentration. No stimulus is sent to the pituitary gland.

❷ Less ADH is secreted into the blood.

❸ Your kidneys become **less permeable** so less water is reabsorbed.

❹ Your bladder fills with a **large quantity of dilute urine**.

If your blood water level becomes **too low** (i.e. not enough water) the opposite happens:

❶ Receptors in your **hypothalamus** detect an increase in salt concentration. A stimulus is sent to the pituitary gland. **Thirst** is stimulated to encourage drinking.

❷ More ADH is secreted into the blood.

❸ Your kidneys become **more permeable** so more water is reabsorbed.

❹ Your bladder fills with a **small quantity of concentrated urine**.

Normal blood water level

Blood

| High blood water level | | Low blood water level |

Hypothalamus

| Receptors detect change | | Receptors detect change |

Pituitary gland

| Less ADH secreted | | More ADH secreted |

Kidneys

| Kidneys reabsorb less water | | Kidneys reabsorb more water |

Bladder

| Large quantity of dilute urine produced | | Small quantity of concentrated urine produced |

Normal blood water level

ADH and Drugs

Drugs such as alcohol and Ecstasy affect the production of ADH in different ways:

- **Alcohol** causes ADH to be **suppressed**, so more water leaves the body in the urine.
- **Ecstasy** causes **too much** ADH to be produced, so too much water remains in the blood. Osmosis then causes the water to leave the blood causing brain cells to swell and burst.

Homeostasis

Diffusion

Diffusion is the overall movement of **substances** from regions of **high** concentration, to regions of **low** concentration.

Substances that move in and out of cells by diffusion include…

- oxygen (O_2)
- carbon dioxide (CO_2)
- dissolved food.

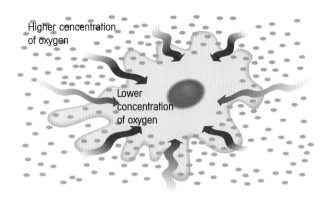

Higher concentration of oxygen

Lower concentration of oxygen

HT Active Transport

Some chemicals can also be moved by active transport. This is the movement of a substance against a concentration gradient (i.e. from a region of low concentration to high concentration). It requires **energy** to do this.

For example, if the concentration of glucose inside a cell is higher than the concentration outside the cell, the glucose would diffuse out of the cell along the concentration gradient. So, cells use active transport to bring all of the glucose back inside the cell.

Osmosis

Osmosis is a type of diffusion. It's the overall movement of **water** from a **dilute solution** to a more **concentrated solution** through a partially permeable membrane.

The membrane allows the passage of water molecules but not solute molecules, which are too large.

Osmosis gradually **dilutes** the concentrated solution.

HT Animal cells, unlike plant cells, don't have a cell wall, which supports the cell membrane, so osmosis can have serious effects:

- If **too much water** enters, the cell could rupture.
- If a **cell loses a lot of water** it won't be able to carry out chemical reactions.

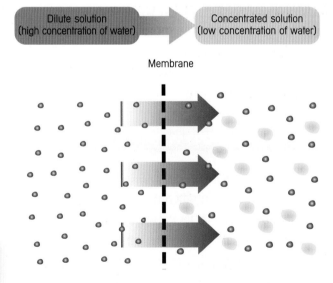

Dilute solution (high concentration of water) → Concentrated solution (low concentration of water)

Membrane

Key Words

Active site • Active transport • **Denatured enzyme** • **Diffusion** • **Enzyme** • **Osmosis**

Enzymes

Enzymes are protein molecules that speed up the rate of chemical reactions in cells (i.e. catalysts in living things).

Enzymes need a specific temperature to work at their **optimum**. Different enzymes have different optimum working temperatures. The graph shows the effect of **temperature** on enzyme activity:

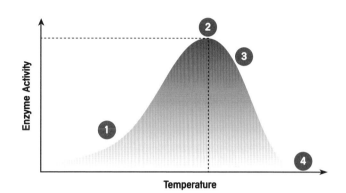

1. At low temperatures, small increases in temperature cause an increase in the frequency and energy of collisions between reactants and enzymes, so the rate of reaction increases.
2. The **optimum enzyme activity** is reached.
3. After the optimum enzyme activity is reached, the enzymes start to get damaged.
4. The enzyme becomes **denatured** (its structure is permanently destroyed and it stops working).

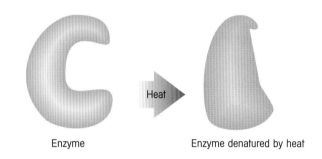

Enzyme   Enzyme denatured by heat

The Lock and Key Model

Only a molecule with the correct shape can fit into an enzyme. This is a bit like a **key** (the molecule) fitting into a **lock** (the enzyme). Once the enzyme and molecule are linked, the following happens:

1. The reaction takes place.
2. The products are released.
3. The process is able to start again.

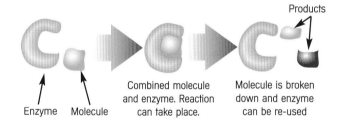

Products

Enzyme Molecule

Combined molecule and enzyme. Reaction can take place.

Molecule is broken down and enzyme can be re-used

HT The Active Site

The active site is the place where the molecule fits into the enzyme. Each enzyme has a different **shape**, so it's highly specific.

The shape of the active site can be changed irreversibly by…

- **heating** the enzyme above a certain temperature
- altering the **pH level**.

This means the molecule can no longer fit and the reaction can't take place.

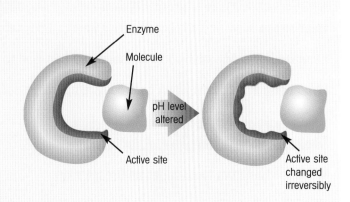

Enzyme

Molecule

pH level altered

Active site

Active site changed irreversibly

Module B4 Summary

Homeostasis

Homeostasis = maintenance of a constant internal environment.

Homeostasis can be affected by **exercise** and **temperature**.

(HT) Homeostasis can also be affected by **blood oxygen levels** and **salt levels**.

Controlling Conditions

Artificial homeostasis – needed when the body's control systems don't work correctly.

Incubators – help premature babies to survive by controlling **temperature** and **oxygen levels**.

Artificial systems and body systems have…
- receptors
- processing centres
- effectors.

(HT) **Negative feedback** – maintenance of a steady state by reversing the change in conditions.

Antagonistic effectors – act as opposites to one another.

Body Temperature

Hot climates ➡ body temperature too high ➡ **sweating**.

Cold climates ➡ body temperature too low ➡ **shivering**.

(HT) **Hypothalamus** – part of the brain responsible for maintaining homeostasis.

Vasodilation = blood vessels in skin dilate in **hot conditions**.

Vasoconstriction = blood vessels in skin constrict in **cold conditions**.

Heat stroke = an uncontrolled increase in your body temperature.

Increased sweating due to hot temperatures can lead to **dehydration**.

Hypothermia – caused when core body temperature falls below 35°C.

Water Inputs and Outputs

Water is input from food, drinks and respiration.

Water is output through sweating, breathing and excretion of faeces and urine.

Water Balance

Kidneys – filter your blood to remove urea and to balance levels of water and other chemicals.

Water level high ➡ kidneys reabsorb less water ➡ large amount of dilute urine.

Water level low ➡ kidneys reabsorb more water ➡ small amount of concentrated urine.

Amount of water that needs to be reabsorbed into blood plasma depends on…
* external temperature
* exercise
* fluid intake
* salt intake.

Alcohol causes large amount of dilute urine to be produced.

Ecstasy causes small amount of concentrated urine to be produced.

HT **Anti-diuretic hormone** – controls concentration of urine. Released into your blood via the **pituitary gland**.

Alcohol ➡ ADH suppressed ➡ more water leaves the body in the urine.

Ecstasy ➡ too much ADH produced ➡ too much water remains in the blood.

Cells

Diffusion = movement of **substances** from high to low concentration.

Substances that move in and out of cells by diffusion include…
* oxygen
* carbon dioxide
* dissolved food.

Osmosis = movement of **water** from high to low concentration.

Active transport = movement of substances against a **concentration gradient** – requires **energy**.

Enzymes

Enzymes = protein molecules that speed up the rate of chemical reactions in cells (catalysts in living things).

Denatured enzyme = structure of the enzyme is permanently destroyed and stops working.

HT **Active site** = place where the molecule fits into the enzyme.

The shape of the active site is affected by…
* **heat**
* **pH level**.

Module B4 Practice Questions

1. Choose the correct words from the options given to complete the following sentence:

   variable   **management**   **constant**   **conditions**   **environment**   **maintenance**

   Homeostasis is the .... of a .... internal ....

2. What happens to the body if homeostasis fails?

   ....

3. If a person is doing strenuous exercise what two changes happen to the body? Tick the correct two options.

   A   Temperature of body decreases ◯   **B**   Temperature of body increases ◯

   C   Water lost via sweat ◯   **D**   Water lost in urine ◯

4. When in a cold climate there is a danger that homeostasis will start to fail. What condition does this cause? Tick the correct option.

   A   Hypothermia ◯   **B**   Warmth excess ◯

   C   Flu ◯   **D**   Hyperthermia ◯

HT 5. **a)**   As well as exercise and temperature, homeostasis can be affected by two other factors. What are these factors?

   i) ....   ii) ....

   b)   List two human activities which can affect these two factors.

   i) ....   ii) ....

6. **a)**   Match the words **A, B, C** and **D** with the spaces numbered **1–4** in the sentence below.

   A   effectors ....   **B**   artificial ....

   C   receptors ....   **D**   processing centres ....

   Body systems and ......**1**...... systems have ......**2**...... to detect stimuli, ...**3**...... to receive information and coordinate responses and ......**4**...... which produce the response automatically.

HT **b)**   What is meant by the term negative feedback?

   ....

7. Name three substances which are moved in and out of cells by diffusion.

   a) ....   b) ....   c) ....

8 This question is about enzymes.

a) On the axes draw the line of enzyme activity you would expect with a typical enzyme.

b) On the graph that you have drawn, add the letter A to show the optimum enzyme activity.

c) What is meant by the term denatured?

....

....

....

Enzyme Activity / Temperature

HT **9** Draw lines between the boxes to match the correct term with the conditions when it takes place.

| Vasodilation |

| Vasoconstriction |

| Cold conditions |

| Hot conditions |

10 Which of the following is not a symptom of heat stroke. Tick the correct option.

A Confusion ⬭

B Fainting ⬭

C Grey skin colour ⬭

D Low blood pressure ⬭

11 a) What organs are responsible for filtering the blood?

....

b) Which of these statements is true? Tick the correct option.

i) When the water level in your body is too high, a large amount of concentrated urine is produced. ⬭

ii) When the water level in your body is too high, a small amount of concentrated urine is produced. ⬭

iii) When the water level in your body is too high, a large amount of dilute urine is produced. ⬭

iv) When the water level in your body is too high, a small amount of dilute urine is produced. ⬭

HT **12** If ADH is secreted into the blood from the pituitary gland, what happens to the urine produced?

....

Growth and Development

Cells

Cells are the building blocks of all living things.

All cells contain...
- **DNA**
- **organelles**.

DNA molecules are in the form of a **double helix** and contain the genetic code.

Organelles are the different parts of the cell's structure. They do different jobs within the cell and work together to allow the cell to perform a specific function.

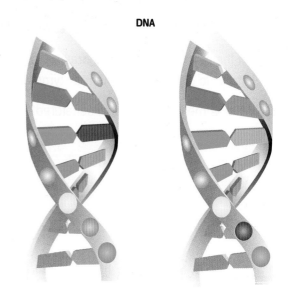

DNA

Animal Cells

Human cells, most animal cells and plant cells have the following parts:
- **Cytoplasm** – where most chemical reactions take place.
- **Nucleus** – contains genetic information.
- **Ribosomes** – where protein synthesis takes place.
- A **cell membrane** – controls movement into and out of the cell.

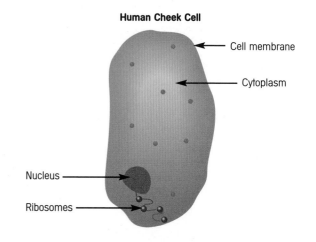

Human Cheek Cell

Cell membrane

Cytoplasm

Nucleus

Ribosomes

Plant Cells

Plant cells also have the following parts:
- A **cell wall** – strengthens the cell.
- A **permanent vacuole** – helps support the cell.
- **Chloroplasts** – absorb light energy to make food.

Key Words

Chromosome • DNA • Gamete • Meiosis • Mitosis • Nucleus • Organelles • Ribosome

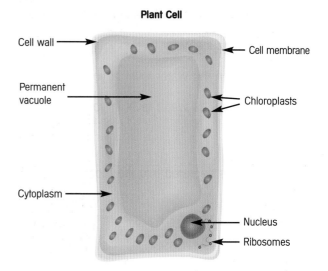

Plant Cell

Cell wall

Cell membrane

Permanent vacuole

Chloroplasts

Cytoplasm

Nucleus

Ribosomes

Mitosis

Mitosis is the division of body cells to produce new cells. Each new cell has…

- **identical** sets of **chromosomes** as the parent cell
- the **same number** of chromosomes as the parent cell
- the same genes as the parent cell.

Mitosis occurs…

- for growth
- for repair
- to replace old tissues.

To enable mitosis to take place, cells go through a cycle of **growth** and then **division**. The cycle repeats itself until the cell can no longer divide.

When a cell enters the **growth phase** of the cycle…

- the number of **organelles increase**
- the **chromosomes** are **copied** – the two strands of each DNA molecule separate and new strands form alongside them.

When a cell enters the **division phase** of the cycle…

- the copies of the **chromosomes separate**
- the cell **divides**.

Parent cell with two pairs of chromosomes.

Each chromosome copies itself.

The copies are pulled apart. Cell now divides for the only time in this mitosis sequence.

Two 'daughter' cells are formed.

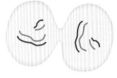

Meiosis

Meiosis only takes place in the **testes** and **ovaries** and is a special type of cell division which produces **gametes** (egg and sperm) for sexual reproduction.

Gametes contain **half** the number of chromosomes as the parent cell.

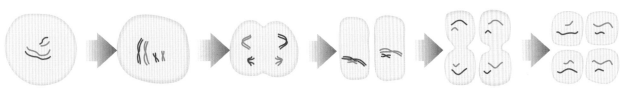

| Cell with two pairs of chromosomes. | Each chromosome replicates itself. | Chromosomes part company and move to opposite sides with their 'copies'. | Cell divides for the first time. | Copies now separate and the second cell division takes place. | Four gametes, each with half the number of chromosomes of the parent cell. |

Growth and Development

Fertilisation

During **fertilisation**, a **male gamete** (sperm) and a **female gamete** (egg) fuse together to produce a single body cell, called a **zygote**.

Gametes only have half the number of **chromosomes** as the parent cell, so the zygote that's produced has **one whole set** of chromosomes.

In each new pair of chromosomes...
- one chromosome comes from the father
- one chromosome comes from the mother.

The zygote then divides by **mitosis** to produce a cluster of cells called an **embryo**.

The embryo continues to develop by mitosis (from one cell to two, to four, to eight, etc.) to eventually become an adult individual.

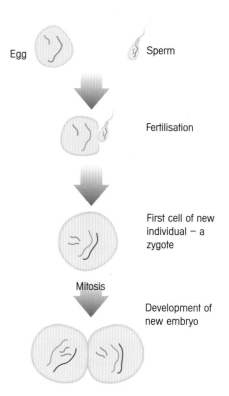

Egg

Sperm

Fertilisation

First cell of new individual – a zygote

Mitosis

Development of new embryo

Variation

Meiosis and **sexual reproduction** produce **variation** between offspring and parents:
- When the gametes fuse, genetic information from two individuals is combined.
- For each gene, just one of each parent's alleles is passed on.
- Each offspring can have a different combination of alleles from either parent.
- The offspring have different characteristics from each other

Genes

Genes are present on the **chromosomes** in each cell **nucleus**.

Genes control...
- growth and development in organisms
- the development of characteristics, e.g. eye colour.

Key Words
Chromosome • Embryo • Fertilisation • Gamete • Gene • Meiosis • Mitosis • Nucleus • Ribosome • Zygote

Genetic Code

Genes control **characteristics** by providing instructions for the production of **proteins**.

The instructions are in the form of a **code**, made up of **four bases** which hold the two strands of the **DNA molecule** together. These bases always pair up in the same way:

- Adenine (A) pairs with thymine (T).
- Cytosine (C) pairs with guanine (G).

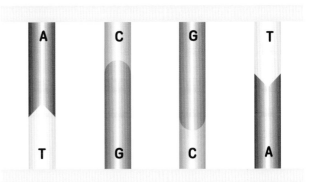

Controlling Growth and Development

DNA is **too large** to leave the nucleus. The genes therefore stay inside the nucleus but the production of proteins takes place **outside** the nucleus, in the **cytoplasm**.

Information stored in the genes has to be transferred into the cytoplasm.

This transfer is done in the following way:

1. The relevant section of DNA is unzipped.
2. Instructions are copied onto smaller molecules called **messenger RNA (mRNA)**.
3. The mRNA leave the nucleus and carry the instructions to the **ribosomes**.
4. The ribosomes follow the instructions to make the relevant protein.

HT The sequence of bases in a gene determines the order in which **amino acids** are joined together to make a particular **protein**.

A group of **three** base pairs codes for one amino acid in a protein chain, called a **triplet code**. There are 20 different amino acids that can be made.

The structure of the protein depends on the amino acids that make it up.

This process is as follows:

1. DNA unravels at the correct gene.
2. A copy of the coding strand is made to produce mRNA.
3. The mRNA copy moves from the nucleus into the cytoplasm.
4. The triplet code is decoded by the ribosomes.
5. Amino acids are joined together to form a polypeptide (protein).

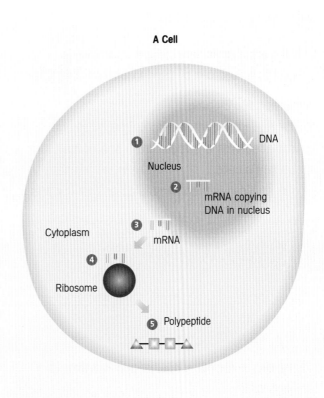

A Cell

Growth and Development

Development of New Organisms

Up to the eight cell stage, all cells in a human **embryo**...
- are unspecialised
- can turn into **any** kind of cell.

These cells are known as **embryonic stem cells**.

After the eight cell stage, the cells in an embryo...
- become **specialised**
- form different types of **tissue**.

The cells contain the **same genes**, but many genes are **not active** because the cell only produces the **proteins** it needs to carry out its role.

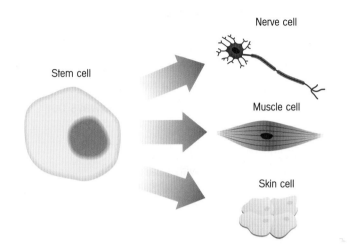

Stem cell

Nerve cell

Muscle cell

Skin cell

HT Stem Cells

Stem cells could potentially be used to...
- help treat diseases and disorders
- repair damage to various tissues.

There are three sources of stem cells:
1. Embryos.
2. Blood from the umbilical cord.
3. Adult stem cells.

Only the **embryonic stem cells** are completely unspecialised and can be used to form any cell type.

In **therapeutic cloning**...
- the nucleus is removed from an egg cell and replaced with a nucleus from one of the patient's cells
- the egg cell is then stimulated so that it starts to divide (as if it were a zygote)
- at the eight cell stage, cells can be removed as they are still unspecialised.

Adult stem cells will only produce cells of a certain type. For example, cells for creating blood cells in bone marrow have to be encouraged to grow more of that type of cell by reactivating (switching back on) inactive genes in the nuclei.

The advantage of using adult cells for growing replacement tissue is that they can be taken from the patient, so the patient's immune system will not reject the transplant.

Replacement tissue can either be grown in a laboratory, or by using a 'host animal' (e.g. a mouse) to maintain a blood supply during growth.

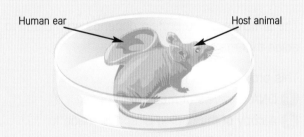

Human ear

Host animal

Key Words

Embryo • Gene • Meristem • Mitosis • Stem cell

Growth and Development

Differentiation in Plants

Plant cells divide by the process of **mitosis**.

New cells in plants specialise into the cells of…
- roots
- leaves
- flowers.

Unlike animals, most plants continue to grow in **height** and **width** throughout their lives.

Meristems

Plant growth occurs in areas called **meristems**, which are sites where **unspecialised cells** divide repeatedly.

These cells then…
- differentiate
- become specialised.

There are **two types** of meristems:
- **Lateral** which leads to increased girth.
- **Apical** which leads to increased height and longer roots.

Some plant cells remain **unspecialised** and can develop into any type of plant cell. These cells allow **clones** of plants with desirable features to be produced from **cuttings**.

If the **hormonal conditions** in their environment are changed, the unspecialised plant cells can develop into other…
- **tissues**, e.g. xylem and phloem
- **organs**, e.g. leaves, roots and flowers.

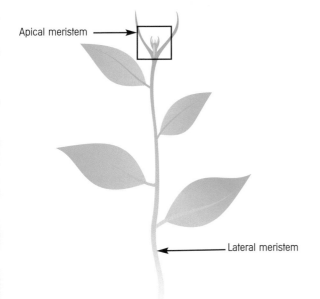

Apical meristem

Lateral meristem

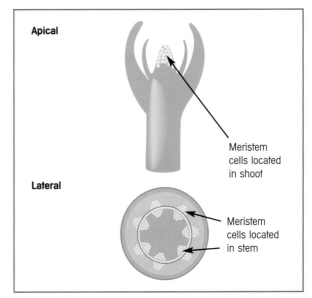

Apical

Lateral

Meristem cells located in shoot

Meristem cells located in stem

Growth and Development

Xylem and Phloem

Xylem tubes are used by the plant to…

- transport water and soluble mineral salts from the roots to the stem and leaves
- replace water lost during transpiration and photosynthesis.

Phloem tubes are used by the plant to transport dissolved food to the whole plant for respiration or storage.

Cross-section of a Stem

Phloem carry food substances up and down the plant

Xylem

Phloem

Xylem vessels carry water up from the roots

Cuttings

Plants can be reproduced in the following way:

1 Cuttings are taken from a plant.

2 The cuttings are put in a rooting hormone.

3 Roots start to form and the new plants develop.

The new plants are **genetically identical** to the parent plant, i.e. they are **clones**.

HT **Auxins** are the main plant hormones used in horticulture, which…

- affect cell division at the tip of a shoot
- cause cells to grow in size just under the tip so that the stem or roots grow longer.

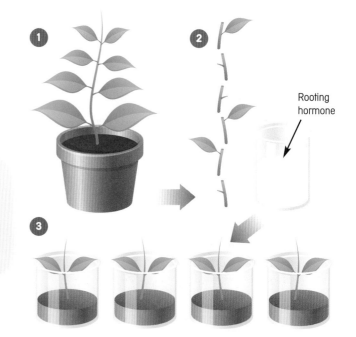

Rooting hormone

Phototropism

Plants respond to light by changing the direction in which they grow. This is called **phototropism**.

They grow towards a light source as they need light to survive.

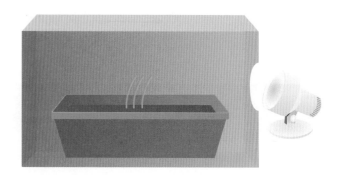

Key Words

Auxin • Clone • Phototropism

HT How Phototropism Works

Auxin is produced at the shoot tip. It moves down the shoot, causing cells further down the shoot to grow.

When light shines on a shoot, auxin moves away from the light source.

This causes the cells furthest away from the light to lengthen, so the shoot bends towards the light source.

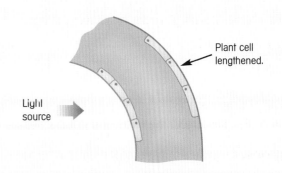

Plant cell lengthened.

Light source

When a light source is directly overhead...
- auxin is evenly spread through the shoot
- the shoot grows **straight** up.

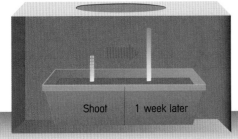
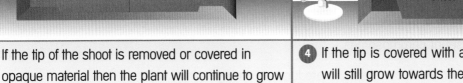

Shoot | 1 week later

2 When a light source is at an angle...
- auxin moves away from the light source
- the auxin is concentrated on the side furthest away from the light
- the shoot **bends** towards the light.

Shoot | 1 week later

If the tip of the shoot is removed or covered in opaque material then the plant will continue to grow upwards – as if the light source was not there.

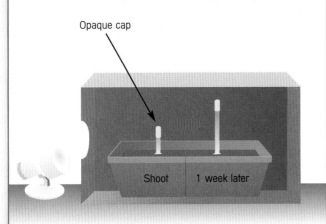

Opaque cap

Shoot | 1 week later

4 If the tip is covered with a transparent cap then it will still grow towards the light source. The same thing will happen if an opaque cylinder is wrapped around the stem leaving the tip exposed.

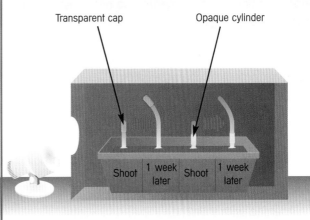

Transparent cap   Opaque cylinder

Shoot | 1 week later | Shoot | 1 week later

Module B5 Summary

Cells

Cells are the building blocks of all living things.

Cells contain...
- DNA
- organelles.

DNA molecules are in the form of a double helix and contain the genetic code.

Organelles = different parts of the cell's structure.

Animal and plants cells have cytoplasm, a nucleus, ribosomes and a cell membrane.

Plant cells also have a cell wall, a permanent vacuole and chloroplasts.

Cell Division

Mitosis = division of body cells to produce new cells. Each new cell contains the same genetic information as the parent cell.

Organelles increase ➡ chromosomes copied ➡ copies of chromosomes separate ➡ cell divides.

Meiosis = division of cells in the testes and ovaries to produce gametes for sexual reproduction.

Gametes – contain half the number of chromosomes as the parent cell.

Fertilisation

During **fertilisation**, a male gamete and a female gamete fuse together to produce a **zygote**.

Zygote – has one whole set of chromosomes.

After fertilisation, the zygote divides by mitosis to produce an **embryo**.

Genes

Genes – present on the **chromosomes** in each cell nucleus.

Genes control...
- growth and development in organisms
- development of characteristics.

Meiosis and sexual reproduction produce **variation** between offspring and parents as genetic information from two individuals is combined.

Genetic code – made up of four bases which hold the two strands of the **DNA molecule** together.

Bases always pair up in the same way:
- Adenine with thymine.
- Cytosine with guanine.

mRNA = small molecules which leave the nucleus and carry genetic information into the cytoplasm.

Ribosomes – follow instructions from the mRNA to make proteins.

HT A group of three base pairs codes for one amino acid in a protein chain, called a triplet code. There are 20 different amino acids that can be made.

Stem Cells

Embryonic stem cells – unspecialised cells that can turn into any kind of cell.

After the eight cell stage, the cells in an embryo become specialised and can form different types of tissue.

HT Stem cells can be used to treat diseases and disorders and repair damage to various tissues.

The three sources of stem cells are embryos, blood from the umbilical cord and adult stem cells.

Plant Growth

New cells in plants specialise into the cells of…
- roots
- leaves
- flowers.

Meristem = area of plant growth, where unspecialised cells divide repeatedly.

Lateral meristem = leads to increased girth.

Apical meristem = leads to increased height and longer roots.

Xylem tubes = transport **water** from the roots to the stem and leaves and replace lost water.

Phloem tubes = transport **dissolved food** to the whole plant for respiration or storage.

Plant Cuttings

New plants develop when cuttings are taken from a plant and put in a rooting hormone. The new plants are clones of the parent plant.

HT **Auxins** = main plant hormones used in horticulture which cause cell growth and division.

Phototropism

Phototropism = growth of plants towards a light source.

HT Light source overhead ➡ auxin spread evenly ➡ shoot grows straight up.

Light source at an angle ➡ auxin on side furthest from light ➡ shoot bends towards light.

1 The diagram shows a human cheek cell.

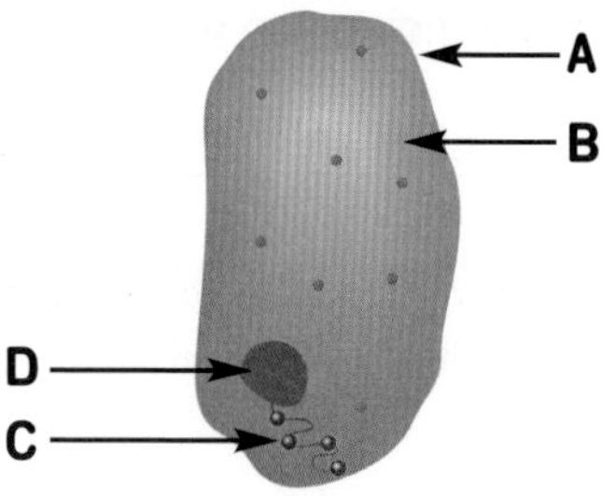

a) Give the names of the parts labelled **A** to **D**.

A .... B ....

C .... D ....

b) Explain what happens inside the ribosomes.

....

2 The four stages, **A**, **B**, **C** and **D**, describe cell growth and division in the cell cycle. They are in the wrong order. Number the stages **1–4** to show the correct order. The first one has been done for you.

A The cell divides.

B The number of organelles increases.

C The chromosome copies move apart from one another.

D The chromosomes are copied.

3 Name the two locations that the process of meiosis can take place in.

a) .... b) ....

4 What is the name given to a fertilised cell? ....

5 a) A section of DNA is shown below. Complete the pairs by writing the correct letters in the boxes provided.

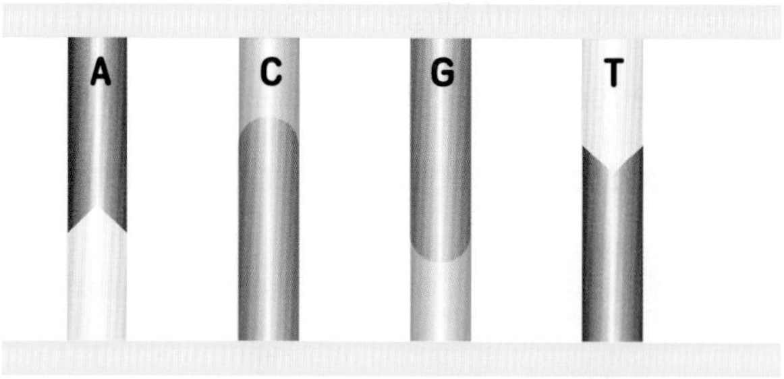

| A | C | G | T |

i) .... ii) .... iii) .... iv) ....

b) DNA is too large to leave the cell. How does the genetic information leave the cell?

....

HT **6 a)** How many bases code for an amino acid? ....

b) How many amino acids can be made using the DNA code? ....

7 **a)** What are the characteristics of stem cells?

....

b) Why can't stem cells be taken after the eight cell stage?

....

8 Fill in the missing word to complete the sentence below:

Plant growth occurs in parts of the plant called ....

9 Describe the roles of the following:

a) Phloem tubes ....

b) Xylem tubes ....

10 Naveen is experimenting with plant shoots and light. She takes a plant shoot and shines light onto it from one side (shown in the diagram below).

a) Draw how the plant shoot would look after 12 hours.

HT **b)** On the plant shoot that you have drawn in part **a)**, add the letter A to show where the plant growth hormone auxin is produced.

c) On what side of the plant shoot will most of the auxin be found?

....

11 What does auxin do to cells?

....

Brain and Mind

The Central Nervous System

A stimulus is a change in an organism's environment.

Animals respond to **stimuli** in order to keep themselves in suitable conditions for survival.

An animal's response is coordinated by the central nervous system (**CNS**). The CNS (brain and spinal cord) is connected to the body by the **peripheral nervous system**.

The peripheral nervous system consists of…
*   **sensory** neurons which carry impulses from receptors to the CNS
*   **motor neurons** which carry impulses from the CNS to effectors.

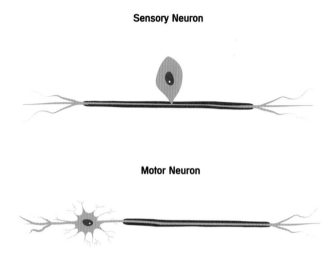

Sensory Neuron

Motor Neuron

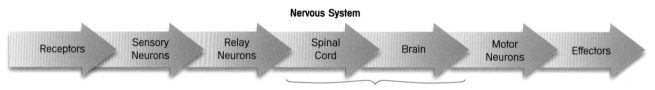

Nervous System

Receptors → Sensory Neurons → Relay Neurons → Spinal Cord → Brain → Motor Neurons → Effectors

The Central Nervous System (CNS)

Receptors and Effectors

Receptors and **effectors** can form part of complex organs, for example…
*   muscle cells in a muscle
*   light receptor cells in the retina of the eye
*   hormone-secreting cells in a gland.

Muscle cells in a muscle – impulses travel along motor neurons and stop at the muscle cells (effectors), causing the muscle cells to contract.

Light receptors cells in the retina of the eye – the lens focuses light onto receptor cells in the retina. The receptor cells are then stimulated and send impulses along sensory neurons to the brain.

Hormone-secreting cells in a gland – an impulse travels along a motor neuron and stops at the hormone-secreting cells in glands (effectors). This triggers the release of the hormone into the bloodstream.

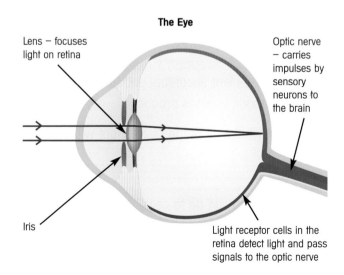

A Motor Neuron

Nucleus

Muscle fibre (effector)

Cell body

The Eye

Lens – focuses light on retina

Optic nerve – carries impulses by sensory neurons to the brain

Iris

Light receptor cells in the retina detect light and pass signals to the optic nerve

Neurons

Neurons are specially adapted cells that carry an **electrical signal** when stimulated:

- They are **elongated** (lengthened) to make connections between different parts of your body.
- They have **branched endings** so that a single neuron can act on many other neurons or effectors.

In **motor neurons** the cytoplasm forms a long fibre surrounded by a cell membrane called an axon.

Some axons are surrounded by a fatty sheath, which…

- insulates the neuron from neighbouring cells
- increases the speed at which the nerve impulse is transmitted.

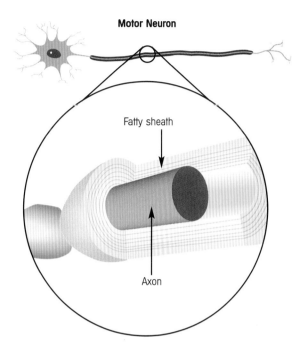

Motor Neuron

Fatty sheath

Axon

Synapses

Synapses are the gaps between adjacent neurons.

HT Impulses are transferred between neurons in the following way:

1. A nerve impulse reaches the synapse through the sensory neuron.
2. The impulse triggers the release of chemicals, called neurotransmitters, into the synapse.
3. Neurotransmitters diffuse across the synapse and bind with receptor molecules on the membrane of a motor neuron.
4. A nerve impulse is sent through the motor neuron.

The receptor molecules only bind with certain chemicals to start a nerve impulse in the motor neuron.

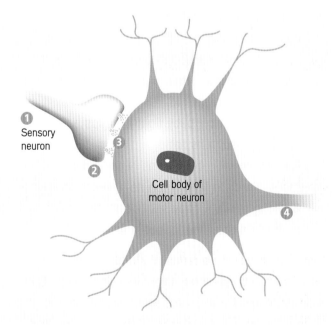

Sensory neuron

Cell body of motor neuron

Key Words

Axon • Central nervous system • Effector • Neuron • Receptor • Stimulus • Synapse

Brain and Mind

Reflex Actions

A **reflex action** is a fast, automatic, involuntary response to a **stimulus**.

The basic pathway for a reflex arc is as follows:

1. A **receptor** is stimulated (e.g. by a sharp pin).
2. This causes impulses to pass along a **sensory neuron** into the spinal cord.
3. The sensory neuron **synapses** with a relay neuron, by-passing the brain.
4. The relay neuron synapses with a motor neuron, sending impulses to the **effectors**.
5. The effectors **respond** (e.g. muscles contract).

Simple reflexes like these ensure that an animal **automatically responds** to a **stimulus** in a way that helps it to survive, for example…

- finding food
- sheltering from predators
- finding a mate.

A majority of the behaviour displayed by simple animals is the result of **reflex actions**. The disadvantage of this is that the animals have difficulty responding to new situations.

Reflex Action Pathway

Stimulus → Receptor → Sensory Neuron → Relay Neuron (in spinal cord) → Motor Neuron → Effector → Response

Simple Reflexes in Humans

Newborn babies exhibit a range of simple reflexes:

- **Stepping reflex** – when held under its arms in an upright position, with feet on a firm surface, a baby makes walking movements with legs.
- **Startle (or moro) reflex** – baby shoots out arms and legs when startled.
- **Grasping reflex** – baby tightly grasps a finger that is placed in its hand.
- **Rooting reflex** – baby turns head and opens mouth ready to feed when its cheek is stroked.
- **Sucking reflex** – baby sucks on a finger (or mother's nipple) that is put in its mouth.

Adults also display a range of simple reflexes. For example, the **pupil reflex** in your eye stops bright light from damaging your retina. Your iris controls the amount of light that enters your eye by contracting various muscle fibres:

- In dim light, your pupil size increases to let more light in.
- In bright light, your pupil size decreases to reduce the amount of light let in.

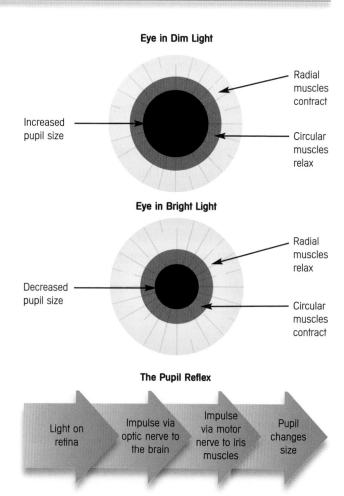

Eye in Dim Light

Increased pupil size

Radial muscles contract

Circular muscles relax

Eye in Bright Light

Decreased pupil size

Radial muscles relax

Circular muscles contract

The Pupil Reflex

Light on retina → Impulse via optic nerve to the brain → Impulse via motor nerve to iris muscles → Pupil changes size

Conditioned Reflexes

A reflex response to a new stimulus can be learned by building an association between the stimulus that naturally triggers the response (**primary stimulus**) and the new stimulus (**secondary stimulus**).

The resulting reflex is called a **conditioned reflex action**.

This effect was discovered at the beginning of the 20th century by a Russian scientist named Pavlov.

Pavlov carried out the following dog experiment:

1 A bell was rung repeatedly whenever meat was shown and given to the dog.

2 Eventually, ringing the bell, without any meat present, caused the dog to salivate.

In a conditioned reflex the final response has **no direct connection** to the stimulus.

Some conditioned reflexes can increase a species' chance of survival.

For example, the caterpillar of the cinnabar moth is black and orange in colour, to warn predators that it's poisonous. After eating a few cinnabar caterpillars, a bird will start to associate these colours with a very unpleasant taste and avoid eating anything that is black and orange in colour.

Simple Reflex

Meat ———→ Salivation

Conditioning

Meat + Sound ———→ Salivation

Conditioned Reflex Action

Sound ———→ Salivation

Modifying Reflex Actions

In some situations your brain can override or modify a reflex action by sending a signal, via a neuron, to the motor neuron in the reflex arc.

For example, this modification allows you to keep hold of a hot plate even though your body's natural reflex response is to drop it.

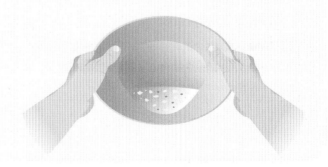

Key Words

Effector • Neuron • Receptor • Reflex action • Stimulus • Synapse

Brain and Mind

Neuron Pathways

Mammals have **complex brains** which contain billions of neurons. This allows them to learn from experience, including how to respond to different situations (**social behaviour**).

In mammals, **neuron pathways** are formed in the brain during development.

The brain grows rapidly during the first few years after birth. As each neuron matures, it sends out multiple branches, increasing the number of synapses.

The way in which a mammal interacts with its environment determines what pathways are formed:

1. Each time you have a new experience, a different neuron pathway is stimulated.
2. Every time the experience is repeated after that, the pathway is strengthened.
3. Pathways which are not used regularly are eventually deleted.
4. Only the pathways that are activated most frequently are preserved.

These modifications mean that certain pathways of your brain become more likely to transmit impulses than others and you will learn how to do a task.

This is why you are able to learn some skills through **repetition**, for example, riding a bicycle, revising for an exam or playing a musical instrument.

A **PET scan** shows neuron activity in parts of the brain in response to learning words through...

- hearing them
- seeing them
- speaking them.

The areas which are stimulated the most, develop more synapses between neurons.

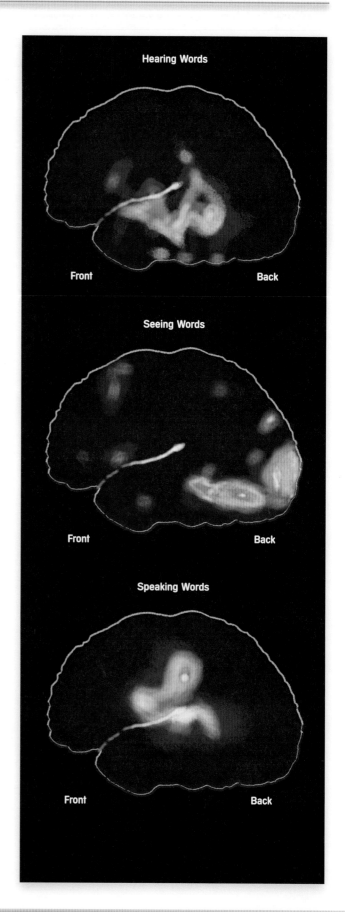

Hearing Words

Front   Back

Seeing Words

Front   Back

Speaking Words

Front   Back

Feral Children

Evidence suggests that children only learn some skills at particular stages in their development.

One example of evidence showing this comes from the study of language development in 'feral children'.

Feral children have been isolated from society in some way, so they don't go through the normal development process.

This isolation can be deliberate (e.g. keeping a child alone in a locked room) or accidental (e.g. through being shipwrecked).

In the absence of any other humans, the children don't ever gain the ability to talk other than to make rudimentary grunting noises.

Learning a language later in development is a much harder and slower process.

Child Development

After children are born there are a series of developmental milestones which can be checked to see if development is following normal patterns.

If the milestones are missing or late it could mean that…
- there are neurological problems
- the child is lacking stimulation.

For example…
- at three months, babies should be able to lift their heads when held to someone's shoulder
- at 12 months, babies should be able to hold a cup and drink from it.

Adapting

The variety of potential pathways in the brain makes it possible for animals to **adapt** to new situations.

For example…
- dogs can be trained to follow spoken commands
- dolphins in captivity can be trained to collect food from a person's hand.

Key Words

Neuron • Synapse

Brain and Mind

Coordination of Senses

The **cerebral cortex** is the part of your brain most concerned with…
- intelligence
- memory
- language
- consciousness.

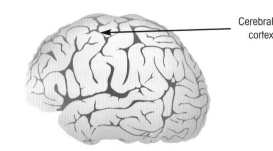

Cerebral cortex

Mapping the Cortex

Scientists have used different methods to map the regions of the cerebral cortex:
- Physiological techniques.
- Electronic techniques.
- Magnetic Resonance Images (MRI) scanning.

Physiological techniques – damage to different parts of the brain can produce different problems, e.g. memory loss, paralysis, or speech loss. Studying the effects of this has led to an understanding of which parts of the brain control different functions.

Electronic techniques – an electroencephalogram (EEG) is a visual record of the electrical activity generated by **neurons** in the brain. Electrodes are placed on the scalp to pick up the electrical signals. By stimulating the patient's **receptors**, the parts of the brain which respond can be mapped.

Magnetic Resonance Imaging (MRI) scanning – this is a relatively new technique that can be used to produce images of different cross-sections of the brain. The computer-generated picture uses colour to represent different levels of electrical activity. The activity in the brain changes depending on what the person is doing or thinking.

Key Words

Cerebral cortex • Neuron • Receptor • Synapse

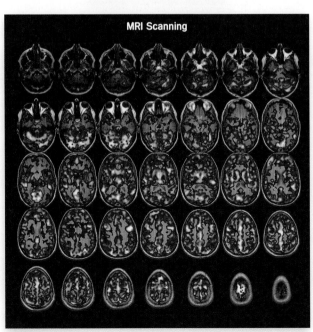

MRI Scanning

Memory

Memory is the ability to **store** and **retrieve** information.

Scientists have produced models to try to explain how the brain does this but, so far, none have been able to provide an good enough explanation.

Verbal memory can be divided into…

- **short-term memory** – stores a limited amount of information for a limited amount of time
- **long-term memory** – stores an unlimited amount of information.

HT You're more likely to remember information if…

- it's repeated (especially over an extended period of time)
- there's a strong **stimulus** associated with it, for example colour, light, smell or sound
- you can see a pattern in it or impose a pattern on it, e.g. the order of the planets can be remembered by imposing a pattern: **M**y **v**ery **e**asy **m**ethod **j**ust **s**peeds **u**p **n**aming **p**lanets - **M**ercury, **V**enus, **E**arth, **M**ars, **J**upiter, **S**aturn, **U**ranus, **N**eptune and **P**luto.

Drugs and the Nervous System

Some drugs and toxins affect the nervous system by changing the speed at which nerve impulses travel to the brain.

They can also…

- send false signals to the brain
- prevent nerve impulses from travelling across synapses
- overload the nervous system with too many nerve impulses.

HT **Serotonin** is a chemical transmitter used in the **central nervous system**. It can have mood-enhancing effects i.e. it is associated with feeling happy.

Serotonin passes across the brain's synapses, landing on receptor molecules. Serotonin not on a receptor is absorbed back into the transmitting neuron by the transporter molecules.

Ecstasy (MDMA) blocks the transporter sites causing serotonin to build up in the synapse. This causes…

- serotonin concentrations in the brain to increase
- the user to experience feelings of elation.

The neurons are harmed in this process and memory loss can be caused in the long term.

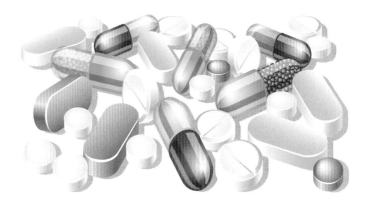

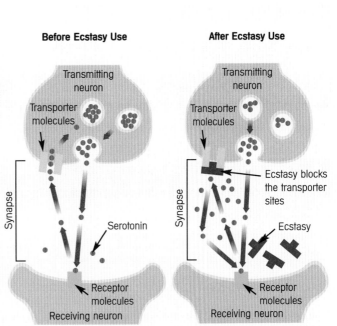

Module B6 Summary

The Central Nervous System

Stimulus = change in organism's environment.

Central nervous system = brain and spinal cord ➤ coordinates animal's responses.

Neurons = specially adapted cells that carry electrical signals when stimulated.

Peripheral nervous system = sensory neurons + motor neurons.

Sensory neurons ➤ carry impulses from receptors to CNS.

Motor neurons ➤ carry impulses from CNS to effectors.

Sensory Neuron

Motor Neuron

Synapses

Synapses = gaps between adjacent neurons.

 Impulses are transferred between neurons in the following way:
1. Nerve impulse moves through sensory neuron.
2. Chemical neurotransmitters are released into synapse.
3. Neurotransmitters diffuse across synapse and bind with receptors on motor neuron.
4. Nerve impulse is sent through motor neuron.

Reflex and Conditioned Actions

Actions increase an animal's chance of survival.

Reflex action = fast, automatic, involuntary response to stimulus.

Receptor stimulated ➤ sensory neuron ➤ relay neuron ➤ motor neuron ➤ effector ➤ response.

HT Conditioned reflex action = association between primary and secondary stimulus. Final response has no direct connection to stimulus.

Modifying a reflex action ➤ brain sends signal to motor neuron.

Neuron Pathways

Neuron pathways form in brain during development.

New experience ➤ neuron pathway stimulated. Repeat experiences strengthens pathways. So skills can be leant through repetition.

Children's Development

Feral children = children who have been isolated at crucial stages of development.

If development milestones missing / late = neurological problems or lacking stimulation.

Variety of potential pathways in brain ➡ animals can adapt to new situations.

Brain

Cerebral cortex deals with…
- intelligence
- memory
- language
- consciousness.

Physiological techniques = studies effects of damage to the brain.

Electronic techniques = visual record of electrical activity generated by neurons in brain.

MRI scans = records different levels of electrical activity of the brain.

Memory

Memory = ability to store and retrieve information.

Short-term memory ➡ limited information for limited time period.

Long-term memory ➡ unlimited amount of information.

HT Information is easier to remember if…
- it's repeated
- there a strong stimulus attached
- there's a pattern to it.

Drugs and the Nervous System

Drugs and toxins…
- affect the nervous system by changing the speed of nerve impulses sent to the brain
- send false signals to brain
- prevent nerve impulses from travelling across synapses
- overload nervous system.

HT Serotonin = chemical transmitter used in nervous system.

Ecstasy ➡ causes a build up of serotonin in brain ➡ damages neurons and can lead to memory loss.

1 (Circle) the correct options in the following sentences:

a) Animals respond to stimuli. These responses are coordinated by the **central nervous system** / **peripheral nervous system**.

b) The system making up the connections of sensory and motor neurons is called the **central nervous system** / **peripheral nervous system**.

c) The brain is an example of an organ in the **central nervous system** / **peripheral nervous system**.

2 What type of neurons do the diagrams below show?

a) ....

b) ....

3 What does a motor neuron do to a hormone-secreting gland when a message is sent?

....

4 Give two functions of the fatty sheath surrounding the axon.

a) ....

b) ....

5 What are synapses?

....

HT The four stages, **A**, **B**, **C** and **D**, describe the sequence of nerve impulse transmission. They are in the wrong order. Number the stages **1–4** to show the correct order. The first one has been done for you.

A Nerve impulse is sent through motor neuron. ◯

B Chemical neurotransmitters are released into synapse. ◯

C Neurotransmitters bind with receptors on motor neuron. ◯

D Nerve impulse moves through sensory neuron. ◯ 1

7 Draw lines between the boxes to match the simple reflexes found in newborn babies to their descriptions.

Stepping reflex	Baby shoots out arms and legs when startled.
Startle (Moro) reflex	Baby sucks on a finger that is put into its mouth.
Grasping reflex	Baby turns head and opens mouth when its cheek is stroked.
Rooting reflex	Baby makes walking movements with legs when held under arms in an upright position.
Sucking reflex	Baby tightly grasps a finger that is placed in its hand.

HT **8** Which of these statements is an example of a conditioned reflex action? Tick the correct option.

A A man choking on a piece of sandwich.

B A girl blinking as she walks from a darkened room into daylight.

C A rabbit stinging itself on a stinging nettle and avoiding the nettles in future.

D A doctor stroking the soles of a patient's feet with a stick.

9 In the past the only way to study the brain was to analyse people who had damaged parts of their brain in accidents. Give the names of two other techniques that enable scientists to 'see' what is going on in the brain.

a) .... **b)** ....

HT **10** What is the term given to children who, either by being deliberately kept from human contact or through being stranded in the absence of humans, grow up without the ability to talk?

....

11 How do drugs in general affect the nervous system?

....

HT **12** Which drug blocks the sites in the brain's synapses where serotonin is removed?

....

Further Biology

Energy Transfer

All living things on Earth ultimately get their **energy** from the Sun. The energy is transferred in the following ways:

- Plants **absorb** a small proportion of the Sun's energy during **photosynthesis**. They store the energy in the chemicals (e.g. starch, cellulose) that make up their cells.
- Energy is **transferred** to other organisms when plants and animals are **eaten** or **decompose**.
- Energy is also transferred when **decay** organisms feed off dead organisms and the waste products of animals.

Ecosystems and Energy Transfer

An **ecosystem** is an area containing a self-sustained community of organisms living in non-living surroundings, e.g. a pond or a wood.

Within an ecosystem there are…

- **autotrophs** (self-feeders), for example, plants that make their own food. They are also known as producers.
- **heterotrophs**, for example, animals and decay organisms that are unable to make their own food so they get their energy by **consuming** other organisms.

Heterotrophs that eat plants are called **herbivores**. They are **primary consumers**.

Heterotrophs that eat other animals are called **carnivores**. They are **secondary** or **tertiary consumers**.

Representing Energy Transfer

The transfer of food energy in an ecosystem can be represented by…

- a food chain
- a pyramid of numbers
- a pyramid of biomass.

Key Words

Autotroph • Carnivore • Ecosystem • Energy • Herbivore • Heterotroph • Photosynthesis

Food Chains

Energy in a food chain always flows in one direction:

1 Light energy flows from the **Sun**.

2 The light energy is transferred to an **autotroph**, which captures the energy, uses it for photosynthesis and stores it in its cells.

3 A **herbivore heterotroph** eats the autotroph. Some energy stored in the plant is transferred and stored in the herbivore's cells.

4 A **carnivore heterotroph** eats the herbivore heterotroph. Some energy is transferred to the carnivore and stored in its cells.

At each stage of the food chain, a large proportion of energy is…

- lost through heat or respiration
- excreted as waste products
- trapped in materials such as bone and fur.

This means **less energy** is available at each stage of energy transfer, which means there's a **limit** to the length of a food chain.

Autotroph

Herbivore heterotroph

Carnivore heterotroph

Carnivore heterotroph

Calculating Energy Efficiency

You can calculate the **energy efficiency** at each stage of a food chain using this formula:

$$\text{Percentage of energy transferred} = \frac{\text{Input energy}}{\text{Output energy}} \times 100$$

Example

This arrow diagram shows the feeding relationship between a green plant, a caterpillar and a bird. Calculate how efficient the energy transfer is for the caterpillar feeding on the plant.

$$\text{Percentage of energy transferred} = \frac{\text{Input energy}}{\text{Output energy}} \times 100$$

$$= \frac{80}{800} \times 100 = \textbf{10\%}$$

N.B. On average only 10% of energy from the Sun ends up stored as plant tissue. If an animal eats a plant, 10% of the energy is used to build up muscle. The rest is used by the animal to respire, move and keep warm.

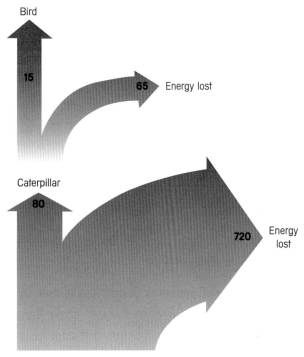

Bird

15

65 Energy lost

Caterpillar

80

720 Energy lost

800 units of energy in plant

Further Biology

Pyramids of Numbers

A **pyramid of numbers**...

- shows the feeding relationships between organisms (autotrophs and heterotrophs) in a food chain
- shows the total number of organisms that feed on each other in a food chain
- uses horizontal bars to represent a different organism (trophic level).

Typically, the bottom bar (the autotroph) is the largest and the top bar (the top consumer) is the smallest. This is because only some of the energy and nutrients are passed on from consumer to consumer.

Pyramids of numbers can have unusual shapes.

For example, an oak tree might have many aphids feeding on it, so the bar representing the oak tree will be smaller than the one representing the aphids. If the aphids are eaten by blue tits, and kestrels eat the blue tits, the pyramid would look like the one opposite.

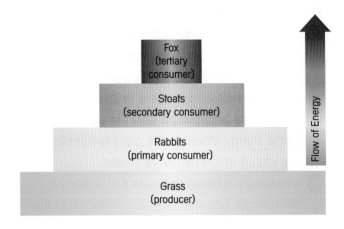

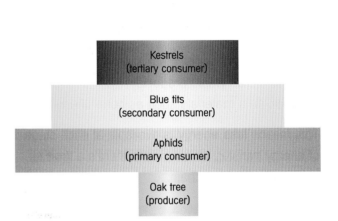

Pyramids of Biomass

A **pyramid of biomass** is a more effective and accurate way of representing feeding relationships.

Each horizontal bar still represents an organism at each stage of the food chain, but instead of recording the **number** of individuals at each level, the pyramid records the **biomass**. (Biomass is the total mass of organisms at each trophic level at a particular time.)

The biomass at each stage will be less than it was at the previous stage.

The advantage of pyramids of biomass is that, by drawing the biomass at each stage to scale, the pyramid will always keep a pyramid shape, reducing the chance of making mistakes in interpretation.

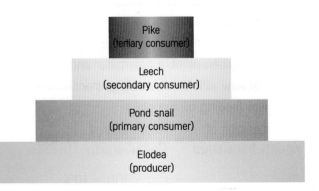

Soil

Soil is comprised of…
- **biomass** – living microorganisms and organisms, and decaying matter
- **inorganic material** – rock, stones and minerals
- **air** – for aerobic respiration
- **water** – helps plants and animals to grow and contains minerals, e.g. nitrates and phosphates.

Calculating Water Mass and Biomass

To calculate the **percentage mass of water** in a soil sample, you should follow this method:

1. Measure the mass of the fresh soil (wet mass).
2. Heat the soil until the water has evaporated.
3. Measure the mass (dry mass).
4. Use these formulae:

| **Water mass in soil** | **=** | **Wet mass** | **—** | **Dry mass** |

| **Percentage of water content** | **=** | $\dfrac{\text{Water mass}}{\text{Wet mass}}$ | **X** | **100** |

To calculate the **biomass content** of soil samples, you should follow this method:

1. Measure the oven dry mass.
2. Heat the sample in an oven for a long time to burn off the organic material.
3. Use these formulae:

| **Biomass** | **=** | **Wet mass** | **—** | **Oven dry mass** |

| **Percentage of biomass** | **=** | $\dfrac{\text{Biomass}}{\text{Wet mass}}$ | **X** | **100** |

Example

a) A sample of soil had a wet mass of 98g. After it had been dried in an oven, it had a dry mass of 57g. Calculate the percentage water content of the soil.

$$\text{Water mass} = \text{Wet mass} - \text{Dry mass}$$
$$= 98g - 57g$$
$$= 41g$$

$$\text{Percentage of water content} = \frac{\text{Water mass}}{\text{Wet mass}} \times 100$$
$$= \mathbf{42\%}$$

b) The mass of the sample after heating in an oven was 39g. Calculate the biomass.

$$\text{Biomass} = \text{Wet mass} - \text{Oven dry mass}$$
$$= 98g - 39g$$
$$= \mathbf{59g}$$

$$\text{Percentage of biomass} = \frac{\text{Biomass}}{\text{Wet mass}} \times 100$$
$$= \mathbf{60\%}$$

Key Words

Biomass • Pyramid of biomass • Pyramid of numbers

Further Biology

Photosynthesis

Photosynthesis takes place in three stages:

1 **Light energy** is absorbed by **chlorophyll** in green plants.

2 Within the chlorophyll molecule, the light energy is used to **rearrange** the **atoms** of carbon dioxide and water to produce glucose (a sugar).

3 Oxygen is produced as a **waste product**.

The equation for photosynthesis is:

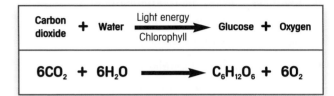

Energy Use in Plants

The **glucose** produced by respiration is…

- used in respiration to **release energy** for the plant in order for other chemical reactions to take place
- converted into **starch** for **storage**
- converted into chemicals that are needed for **plant cell growth**, for example, cellulose, protein, chlorophyll.

Glucose is a **soluble** chemical, but when it's stored in a plant, it's converted into an **insoluble** long-chained carbohydrate molecule called starch.

Long-chained molecules that are made up of many copies of the same unit are called **polymers**. Starch is a polymer because it's made up of millions of glucose molecules joined together.

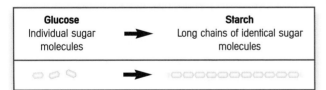

Cellulose is a carbohydrate. It's needed by the plant to build cell walls. It has a similar structure to starch but the long chains are cross-linked to form a mesh.

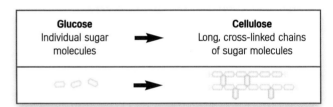

Glucose, together with **nitrates** absorbed by the soil, can be converted into **amino acids**. Amino acids can be linked together in different combinations to make **protein**, which is a polymer.

HT Plants need to absorb nitrates from the soil for healthy growth. Plants normally absorb nutrients by **diffusion**, but the concentration of nitrates outside the plant is lower than that inside. Therefore, a plant has to use **energy** to absorb nitrates by **active transport**.

HT Maintaining the Osmotic Balance

Cells contain water. If a plant cell doesn't contain any dissolved glucose, water moves in and out at the same rate, so it is **osmotically balanced**.

If glucose dissolves in the cell water, it changes the osmotic balance to favour net water movement into the cell, i.e. the less-concentrated water outside the cell will flow into the cell by osmosis.

This causes the cell to swell (become turgid). The cell isn't osmotically balanced.

Glucose is stored in cells in the form of starch grains. Starch is a better storage molecule than glucose because it's an insoluble chemical, which means that it doesn't alter the osmotic balance within a cell.

Limiting Factors for Photosynthesis

These factors can all limit the rate of photosynthesis:
- Temperature.
- Carbon dioxide concentration.
- Light intensity.

Any one of these factors, at a particular time, may be the limiting factor.

Accurate measurements of the rate of photosynthesis can be hard because it's difficult to measure without altering one of the limiting factors.

Factors that affect photosynthesis are difficult to control, e.g. wind or moisture levels.

Measurements only **indicate** the rate of photosynthesis rather than give a definite rate.

Key Words

Active transport • **Chlorophyll** • **Insoluble** • **Photosynthesis** • **Soluble**

(HT) Temperature

1 As the temperature rises, so does the rate of photosynthesis. So, temperature is limiting the rate of photosynthesis.

2 As the temperature approaches 45°C, the enzymes controlling photosynthesis start to be destroyed and the rate of photosynthesis drops to zero.

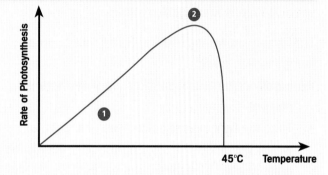

Carbon Dioxide Concentration

1 As the carbon dioxide concentration rises, so does the rate of photosynthesis. So, carbon dioxide is limiting the rate of photosynthesis.

2 A rise in carbon dioxide levels now has no effect. Carbon dioxide is no longer the limiting factor. It must be either light or temperature.

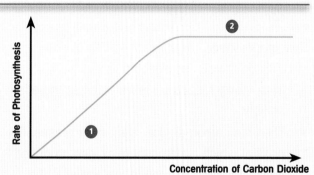

Light Intensity

1 As the light intensity increases, so does the rate of photosynthesis. So, light intensity is limiting the rate of photosynthesis.

2 A rise in temperature now has no effect. Light intensity is no longer the limiting factor. It must be either carbon dioxide or temperature.

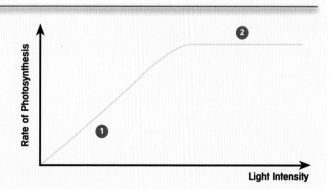

Further Biology

HT Compensation Point

Photosynthesis in green plants only takes place during daylight. During a 24-hour period there's a point at which the **rate of photosynthesis** exactly **matches** the **rate of respiration**. This means that...

- the amount of carbon dioxide used in photosynthesis exactly matches the amount produced in respiration
- the amount of oxygen produced in photosynthesis exactly matches the amount used in respiration at that point in time.

This is known as the compensation point and, depending on which is the limiting factor, it's the point at which there's just enough light or carbon dioxide for a plant to survive (i.e. the light compensation point or the CO_2 compensation point).

At the compensation point, all the food produced by photosynthesis is used up in respiration.

Graphs of the Compensation Point

Graphs can be used to show the compensation point. In these graphs, the amount of oxygen produced has been used to indicate photosynthesis.

This graph shows the effect of light intensity on the compensation point:

- Initially only respiration takes place as there is no light.
- Then the light intensity increases. The point at which the amount of oxygen produced equals the amount used in respiration is the **light compensation point**.

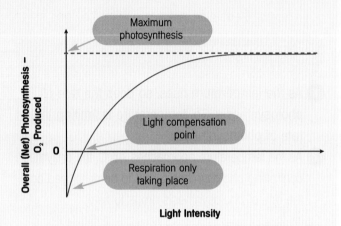

This graph shows the effect of carbon dioxide intensity on the compensation point:

- Initially only respiration takes place as there is no light.
- Then the carbon dioxide intensity increases. The point at which the amount of oxygen produced equals the amount used in respiration is the **carbon dioxide compensation point**.

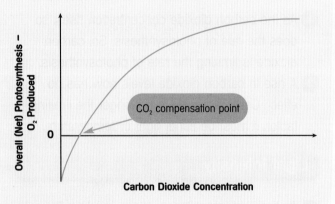

Key Words

Compensation point

⒣ Graphs of the Compensation Point (cont.)

The level of photosynthesis over a 24-hour period can be plotted and analysed to identify the processes taking place. This graph can be interpreted to give information about the rate of photosynthesis and respiration:

- During the night photosynthesis stops, but respiration still takes place. Therefore, the net amount of carbon dioxide produced is high, and oxygen used in respiration drops.
- During the day, respiration continues and photosynthesis takes place. Net carbon dioxide released is low and oxygen released is high.
- The compensation point is where the lines cross.

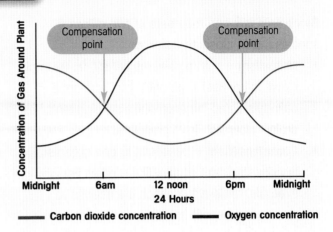

Human Activity and CO₂ Levels

As part of the Intergovernmental Panel on Climate Change (IPCC), over 2500 scientists agreed that human activities such as burning fossil fuels were most likely to be the cause of the increasing levels of carbon dioxide in the atmosphere, known as the **Enhanced Greenhouse Effect**.

If nothing is done to reduce the amount of CO_2 being put into the atmosphere, the Earth's temperature will increase, causing…

- polar ice caps to melt
- sea levels to rise, flooding low-level countries
- the extinction of entire species, e.g. the polar bear.

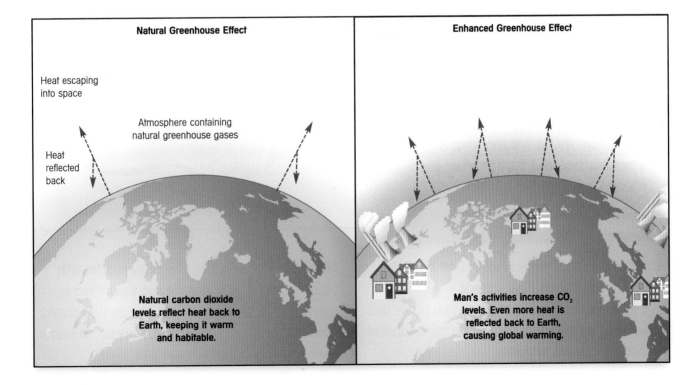

Further Biology

Symbiosis

Symbiosis is when members of two different species live in close association:

- **Mutualism** – both organisms benefit, for example, clownfish protect anemones from anemone-eating fish, and the anemone's stinging tentacles protect clownfish from predators.
- **Commensalism** – beneficial to one organism, but doesn't harm or benefit the other. For example, remora fish attach themselves to sharks and benefit from this as they're transported through the sea, feeding off food scraps. It has no effect on the shark.
- **Parasitism** – beneficial to one organism (the **parasite**) and harmful to the other (the **host**). A parasite can't survive without its host. For example, tapeworms and leeches are parasites found in mammals.

Key Words

Commensalism • Evolution • Host • Mutualism • Parasite • Parasitism • Symbiosis

Evolution of Parasites

A parasite's body is specifically adapted to survive within a particular host. The **evolution** of the parasite is closely linked to that of the host.

Tapeworms live inside the intestines of the host (the human), absorbing the food that the host eats. The tapeworm's shape and features are adapted for its function:

- The top of the tapeworm has suckers and teeth-like structures to hold onto the inside of the intestine.
- Tapeworms are flat and very long, so they have a large surface area through which to line the intestine and absorb food.

Leeches attach to the skin of a mammal (the host) and suck their blood. A leech...

- has a sucker at each end of its body – one sucker attaches the leech to the host, whilst the other sucks the host's blood
- excretes an anticoagulant to stop the blood from clotting as it feeds.

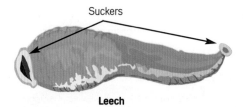

Suckers

Leech

Problems with Parasites

Parasites can cause many problems, for example...

- they cause diseases, e.g. malaria
- they affect food production (from both plants and animals) as a parasite can reduce the amount of food that can be harvested.

Malaria is a disease that kills many people each year. It's carried by a parasite and transmitted to people by the female mosquito. The disease breaks down the body's red blood cells. Malaria can lead to fever, anaemia, organ damage and death.

HT Sickle-Cell Anaemia

Sickle-cell anaemia is a **disorder** that affects the haemoglobin in red blood cells.

If a person has sickle-cell anaemia, they have an abnormal form of haemoglobin which makes their red blood cells change shape until they become sickle-shaped. These deformed blood cells block blood vessels and deprive the body's tissues and organs of oxygen.

These are some of the symptoms of sickle-cell anaemia:
- Anaemia.
- Feeling weak and tired.
- Painful cramps and pain in joints.
- Eyesight problems.

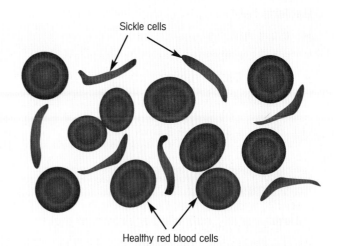

Sickle cells

Healthy red blood cells

Inheritance of Sickle-Cell Anaemia

Sickle-cell anaemia is a **hereditary disorder** that occurs when a person inherits two faulty **recessive alleles** (one from each parent).

If a person inherits…
- **two** faulty alleles they will have the disorder
- **one** faulty allele they will be a carrier. They may have some of the symptoms of sickle-cell anaemia.

If a carrier reproduces with another carrier, there's a 25% chance they will pass on full sickle-cell anaemia to their offspring.

	Carrier	x	Carrier
Parents	Ss	x	Ss

Sex cells: S s S s

Offspring: SS Ss Ss ss

Unaffected Carrier Carrier Affected

s = sickle cell allele   S = healthy allele

Sickle-Cell Anaemia and Malaria

Malaria can harm or kill people who have normal haemoglobin. This means that in areas where malaria is common, the number of people with normal haemoglobin in the population will decrease.

In general, a person who inherits two sickle-cell alleles is less likely to be able to reproduce and pass on their genes. However, sickle cells aren't infected by malaria parasites, so a person with one sickle-cell allele (a carrier) is more likely than a non-carrier to recover from a severe attack of malaria.

So, in areas where malaria is common, carriers are more likely to reproduce and pass on their genes to their offspring, than people who either have normal alleles, or who have two sickle-cell alleles.

This means the number of people who carry the faulty gene will increase, causing the frequency of the sickle-cell allele to be higher than it would be if malaria didn't exist.

This is an example of **natural selection.**

Further Biology

The Structure of Bacteria

Bacteria have…
- a cell wall
- a cell membrane
- circular **DNA** chromosomes – the DNA is not in a nucleus

HT Bacteria also have a DNA plasmid.

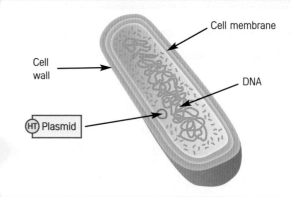

Fermentation

A **fermenter** is a **controlled environment** that has ideal conditions for microorganisms to live in, feed and produce the proteins needed.

Fermenters can be used to grow…
- microorganisms or their products, for example, industrial quantities of **antibiotics**
- **single-cell proteins**, for example, mycoprotein (the main ingredient of Quorn™, a meat substitute)
- **enzymes** that can be used in food production, for example, rennin, which is used in cheese-making.

Genetic Modification

DNA contains the code for the protein a particular organism needs. Proteins produced by one organism may not be produced by another.

By carrying out genetic modification, the gene that produces a desirable protein can be inserted into another organism so that it too produces the right protein.

This is how **genetic modification** is carried out:

1 The desired gene is selected and **isolated**.

HT The desired gene is inserted into the target bacterium using a vector, i.e. a **virus** or a **plasmid**.

2 The gene is **replicated**, i.e. it is copied exactly to make the number of genes increase.

3 The gene is then **inserted** / **transferred** into the target organism.

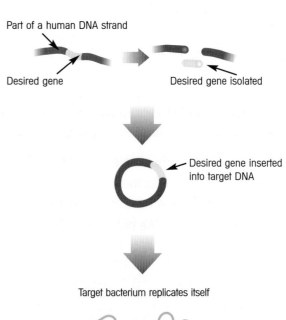

Part of a human DNA strand

Desired gene   Desired gene isolated

Desired gene inserted into target DNA

Target bacterium replicates itself

Bacterium

Advantages and Disadvantages of Genetic Modification

Genetic modification has the potential to solve many problems for society. For example, it can be used to…

- produce healthier crops with greater yields
- produce disease-resistant crops, which reduces the need for pollution-causing pesticides
- enable some crops (e.g. bananas) to naturally carry vaccines so they don't need to be kept refrigerated
- allow organisations to monitor the release and spread of genetically modified crops by looking for antibiotic-resistant markers in crops (the markers will only be there if the crop has been modified)
- enable some drugs (e.g. insulin) to be made from human, rather than animal, DNA.

However, there are also drawbacks with genetic modification:

- Genetically modified organisms may be expensive.
- There may be unknown effects on ecosystems.
- Crops that have been modified may pass the genes on to other non-modified crops and weeds. This would lead to resistance in weeds and the need to use more pesticides.
- The antibiotic resistance may be passed on.
- Some people disagree with genetic modification on **ethical** grounds, so they will not buy genetically modified products.

Genetic Testing

The following method is used to test a gene:

1. DNA is isolated from the nucleus of a white blood cell. The DNA is often amplified so that there's enough material to experiment with. It's then broken up into different sized pieces.
2. A gene probe is created. This is a single-stranded DNA or RNA sequence that has bases that pair up with the complementary bases on the target gene. The probe will only attach if the desired gene is present in a sample.
3. UV or **autoradiography** is used to locate the gene probe:
   - If the probe has a marker that causes it to fluoresce when UV light is shone onto it, then UV light is used to locate it.
   - If the probe has a radioisotope (which emits radioactive particles), X-ray film can be used to locate it. This is called **autoradiography**.

INSULIN

Key Words

Autoradiography • Bacteria • DNA • Ethical • Fermenter • Genetic modification • Plasmid • Vector

Further Biology

Respiration

Respiration is the **release of energy** from food chemicals. There are two types of respiration:

- Aerobic respiration.
- Anaerobic respiration.

Aerobic Respiration

Aerobic respiration releases energy inside living cells by breaking down and combining glucose molecules with **oxygen**.

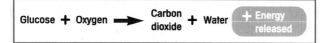

Glucose + Oxygen ⟶ Carbon dioxide + Water + Energy released

HT Energy released in respiration is used to synthesise a chemical called adenosine triphosphate (ATP), which…

- transfers energy from chemical bonds to the reactions that require energy within the cell
- is often referred to as the **energy currency** of living things.

Respiration in Action

Muscles are made up of tissues that contract and relax. When muscles are working, they need more energy than when they are at rest. The energy to contract comes from respiration.

HT The energy to contract comes specifically from the chemical ATP.

During exercise…

- **respiration increases** in order to deliver a faster supply of glucose and oxygen to the muscles so they are able to move and work faster
- the **heart rate increases** in order to pump more blood around the body and to remove the increased levels of carbon dioxide (waste product) produced by the faster rate of respiration
- the **breathing rate increases** in order to ensure that there's enough oxygen circulating round the body in the blood cells.

Instead of a single measurement, a **range** of values is given for a healthy heart rate or blood pressure. However, someone may fall outside the range and still be healthy.

Anaerobic Respiration

Anaerobic respiration releases energy inside living cells by breaking down glucose molecules in the **absence of oxygen**, i.e. without oxygen.

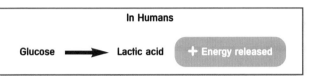

In Humans

Glucose ⟶ Lactic acid + Energy released

Anaerobic respiration…
- takes place when not enough oxygen can get to the muscles (e.g. during vigorous exercise)
- produces short bursts of energy
- is less efficient and produces less energy than aerobic respiration
- produces **lactic acid**, which builds up in the muscle cells, so the body can't use anaerobic respiration to produce energy for long periods of time.

HT Aerobic respiration releases more energy per glucose molecule than anaerobic respiration:
- Aerobic respiration produces 32 ATP per glucose molecule.
- Anaerobic respiration produces 2 ATP per glucose molecule.

Although the amount of energy released from anaerobic respiration is comparatively low, being able to respire with low levels of oxygen is an advantage when escaping from danger, e.g. running from a predator.

The extra few seconds where a human or other organism can continue to run could mean the difference between life and death.

HT Oxygen Debt

Lactic acid is toxic and can cause harm to muscle cells if it's not removed. After anaerobic respiration has stopped, the lactic acid needs to be broken back down into carbon dioxide and water, which can then be removed from muscle cells via the blood.

Therefore, after vigorous exercise there is a time period before the body can return to normal functions. Extra oxygen is needed to break down the lactic acid – this is called the oxygen debt.

Further Biology

Parts of Blood

The functions of the four components of blood are described in this table:

Part of Blood	Function
Red blood cells	Transport oxygen from the lungs to the organs
White blood cells	Fight infection and defend the body against microorganisms
Platelets	Clot together at injury sites to prevent blood from leaving the body
Plasma	Transports substances around the body

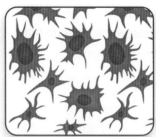
Platelets

Plasma

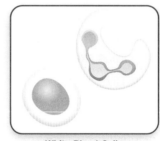
White Blood Cells

Red Blood Cells

Blood Types

The **ABO system** is a way of classifying blood types. There are four main blood types:

- A
- B
- AB
- O

On the surface of the red blood cells are **antigens**, and in the blood plasma there are **antibodies**. The types of antigens and antibodies present in blood determines the ABO type.

ABO Blood Type	Presence of Antigen or Antibody			
	Antigen A	Antigen B	Anti-A Antibody	Anti-B Antibody
A	Yes	No	No	Yes
B	No	Yes	Yes	No
O	No	No	Yes	Yes
AB	Yes	Yes	No	No

ABO Compatibility

In a blood transfusion…
- the patient receiving blood is called the **recipient**
- the person donating blood is called the **donor**.

It's very important that the **antigens** in the donor's blood are **matched** to those present in the recipient's blood, otherwise the antibodies in the recipient's blood could react with the donor's blood.

For example, if a donor whose blood contained anti-B antibodies is transfused into a recipient with antigen B, the recipient's blood would clot, causing circulation problems and possibly death.

Key Words

ABO system • Antibody • Antigen • Co-dominant • Donor • Recipient

Matching Donors and Recipients

People with blood type O…
- are universal donors because their blood type doesn't contain either antigen
- can only receive blood from donors who also have blood type O because their blood carries both antibodies.

People with blood type AB…
- are universal recipients because their blood contains both antigens so it doesn't matter if the donated blood has all, or none, of the antigens
- can only donate blood to people with AB blood.

Blood Type Compatibility

To interpret blood type compatibility, you need to identify the recipient's antibodies and then see if the donor has antigens that match the antibodies.

The following method is used:
1. Mix half of a blood sample with a serum containing anti-A antibodies.
2. Mix the other half of the blood sample with a serum containing anti-B antibodies.
3. See if either of the blood samples clots. (Clotting indicates the ABO type).

Example
A blood sample clots when it is mixed with the anti-A antibody, but not when it is mixed with the anti-B antibody. What blood type is it?

The clotting indicates that antigen A is present but not antigen B. Therefore, the blood type is A.

HT Blood Group Genetics

Blood type is carried on a single gene on the ninth chromosome. It can have one of three alleles (matching the blood types), i.e. A, B or O:
- Alleles A and B are co-dominant.
- The O allele is recessive.

If both parents have blood group O, then their children will have blood group O, because O is recessive so it means no other alleles are present.

You can draw genetic diagrams to illustrate the inheritance of ABO blood types.

Example
Draw a genetic diagram for the alleles the offspring could have if one parent has blood type AB and the other parent has blood type A.

The parent that has blood type AB would have A and B alleles. The parent that has blood group A could have AA alleles, or AO alleles. So, you need to draw two genetic diagrams.

1

	A	B
A	AA	AB
O	AO	BO

2

	A	B
A	AA	AB
A	AA	AB

1. There is a 50% chance that offspring will have blood type A, 25% chance they will have blood type AB, and 25% chance they will have blood type B.
2. There is a 50% chance that offspring will have blood type A, and 50% chance they will have blood type AB.

Further Biology

The Heart

Most of the heart wall is made of muscle. The left side is more muscular than the right because it pumps blood around the whole body (whereas the right side pumps blood only to the lungs).

The heart has four chambers:

- Two **atria** – the smaller, less muscular upper chambers that receive blood coming back to the heart from the veins.
- Two **ventricles** – the larger, more muscular lower chambers.

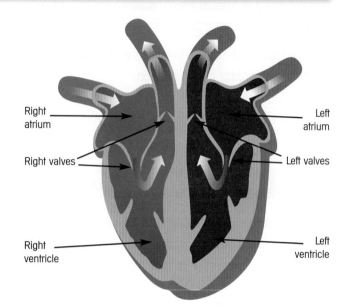

The Double Circulatory System

This is the cardiac cycle:

- The heart muscles **relax** and blood flows into the atria through veins from the lungs and the rest of the body.
- The atria **contract**, squeezing blood into ventricles.
- The ventricles **contract** and blood is forced out of the lower chambers, which carry the blood to the body and lungs.
- The heart muscles **relax** and the whole process starts again.

Valves in the heart and veins ensure that the blood flows in the right direction (i.e. not backwards).

Humans have a **double circulation system**, which means that the blood returns to the heart twice on every circuit of the body:

- **Deoxygenated** blood that has travelled around the body enters the heart via the right atrium.
- It's pumped from the heart into the lungs, where haemoglobin binds to the oxygen, becoming **oxyhaemoglobin**.
- The **oxygenated** blood returns to the heart via the left atrium and is then pumped to the rest of the body.

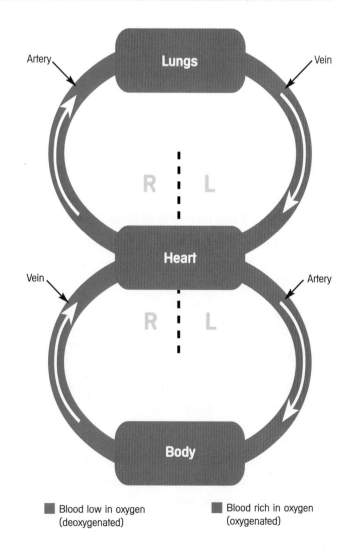

Blood Vessels

There are three types of blood vessel:

- **Arteries** carry blood away from the heart towards the organs. They have thick, elastic walls to cope with the high pressure of blood coming from the heart. Substances can't pass through the artery walls.
- **Veins** carry blood from the organs back to the heart. They have thinner, less elastic walls and contain valves to prevent the blood flowing backwards. Substances can't pass through the vein walls.
- **Capillaries** connect arteries to veins. They have a narrow, thin wall that is only one cell thick. The exchange of substances between cells and the blood takes place here.

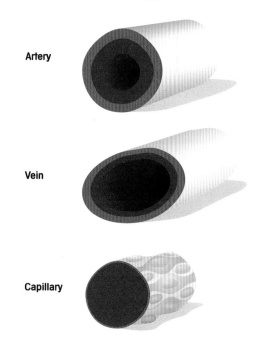

Artery

Vein

Capillary

Tissue Fluid

The plasma of arterial blood contains the dissolved products from digestion. Around the body tissues are networks of capillaries called capillary beds. The blood flow in **capillary beds** is very slow so plasma leaves and becomes **tissue fluid**.

Tissue fluid…

- enables the nutrients required by the cells (e.g. glucose needed for respiration, oxygen and hormones) to diffuse into the tissue cells
- collects and carries away some cellular waste products, such as carbon dioxide and urea.

Most of the tissue fluid returns to the capillary bed where it again becomes plasma and continues its journey through the body, this time in the veins.

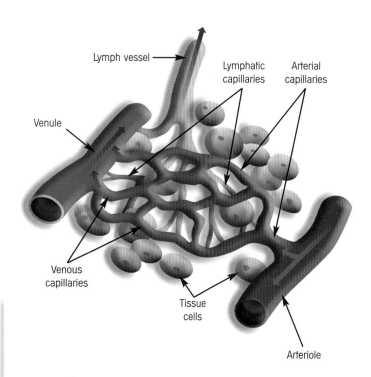

Lymph vessel

Lymphatic capillaries

Arterial capillaries

Venule

Venous capillaries

Tissue cells

Arteriole

Key Words

Artery • Atria • Capillary • Deoxygenated •
Double circulation system • Oxygenated •
Oxyhaemoglobin • Valve • Vein •
Ventricle

Further Biology

The Skeletal System

Vertebrates have an internal skeleton that…
- provides **support**
- enables **movement**
- **protects** internal organs.

Bones, muscles, tendons and ligaments combine so that joints can move easily and carry out work:
- **Bones** are rigid tissues that make up the skeleton.
- **Muscle** is tissue that contracts and relaxes.
- **Ligaments** are tough, fibrous, elastic connective tissues that connect **bones** together in a joint.
- **Tendons** are tough, fibrous, elastic connective tissues that connect **muscle to bone** or **muscle to muscle**.

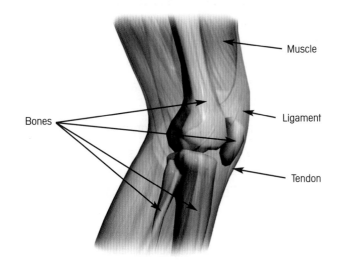

Joint Movement

Muscles can only move bones by **contracting**, so they work in **antagonistic pairs**, i.e. one muscle contracts whilst another muscle relaxes. For example…
- to lift the lower arm, the biceps contracts and the triceps relaxes
- to lower the arm, the triceps contracts and the biceps relaxes.

If the tendon connecting the triceps to the bone were to be cut, the triceps wouldn't be able to contract and the arm would remain in the up position.

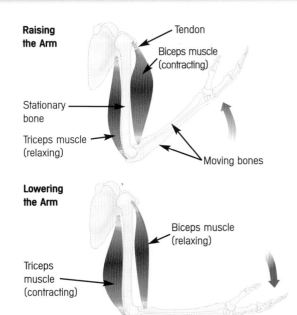

Cartilage and Synovial Fluid

Joints are covered by a smooth layer of **cartilage**. Cartilage is a tough connective tissue that helps reduce wear and tear in a joint by preventing the bones rubbing together.

Synovial fluid is an oily fluid. It enables the joint to move freely by reducing friction and cushioning the joint against bumps and knocks.

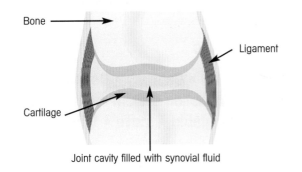

Medical History Assessment

Practitioners, for example, doctors, registered nurses, fitness instructors and opticians, are specially trained to help you maintain and improve your health and fitness.

Before they can recommend treatment or an exercise programme, a practitioner needs to know the following information about a patient's medical or lifestyle history:

Symptoms – visible or noticeable effects on the body, which can be used to identify a problem.

Current medication – different medicines can sometimes conflict with one another.

Alcohol consumption – excessive alcohol intake can cause…
* weight gain
* damage to the liver and kidneys
* interference with some medications.

Tobacco consumption – smoking has been directly linked with…
* lung cancer
* heart disease
* high blood pressure.

Family medical history – some medical conditions can be genetic (inherited). It's important to know if any particular conditions run in your family.

Previous treatments – if you have recurring symptoms you might need a different **diagnosis** or to see a specialist.

A practitioner must properly assess a patient before any diagnostic tests are carried out in order to make sure that the treatment recommended is effective and will not make their condition worse, or cause another problem.

The risk of carrying out any tests must be assessed and balanced against the chances of being able to cure or reduce the symptoms.

Key Words

Antagonistic pairs • Bone • Diagnosis • Ligament • Muscle • Symptom • Tendon • Vertebrate

HT Recording Information

A person's medical or fitness information must be…
* recorded
* stored
* made available to other people on the practitioner's team.

If the patient's usual practitioner is unavailable it means another practitioner can read the patient's notes and continue the treatment without having to start the diagnosis from the beginning.

It is also important to store information in case anything happens to the patient in the future. If necessary, records can be checked to see if there were errors in diagnosis so that procedures can be changed.

In the very rare cases that a practitioner doesn't follow procedures, the records can then be used as evidence to prosecute.

Further Biology

Treatment

Depending on the **diagnosis**, the practitioner will decide which treatment or method will be used to improve the patient's health or fitness.

There is often more than one way to achieve an agreed target. For example, the problem could be solved by…
- greater levels of fitness
- a period of recovery
- rehabilitation, e.g. learning how to walk again after an accident.

All treatments carry some risk, for example, a treatment could cause further harm or have side effects. The practitioner has to weigh the known risks against the benefits gained.

The patient must be made aware of the risks and likelihood of success so that they can make an informed decision before consenting.

Monitoring and Assessing Progress

A treatment or fitness training programme needs to be monitored to check that it's having the desired effect. It can then be modified depending on the patient's progress.

A programme might be modified before completion if…
- the patient is finding the programme too hard (the problem could continue or a new injury could occur)
- the patient is finding the programme too easy (progress would be slow and the patient might not recover fast enough).

One way of monitoring progress during training is to measure the **pulse rate** or **aerobic fitness** of a patient / client. A patient who is increasing their aerobic fitness should lower their heart rate and have a faster recovery rate.

Regular contact between a patient and a practitioner has many benefits.

The practitioner has the opportunity to become more familiar with the medical history and background of the patient, and the patient will feel more comfortable and reassured if they see the same practitioner each time.

After treatment or training is complete, the patient can be called back for a check-up. Questions about progress and issues are asked and sometimes tests are carried out, e.g. the pulse rate might be checked.

Recording Progress

It is essential that accurate records are kept during treatment or fitness training because the records can be used to assess progress and determine trends.

HT Inaccurate records could slow down progress or even make a condition worse. However, progress records need to take into account the accuracy and reliability of the recording techniques.

Injuries Caused by Excessive Exercise

If a person over-exerts themselves by doing excessive exercise, they can cause themselves the following injuries:

- **Sprains**.
- **Dislocations**.
- Torn **ligaments** or **tendons**.

Sprains

The following are **symptoms** of a sprain:
- **Swelling** due to fluid building up at the site of the sprain.
- **Pain** – the joint hurts and may throb.
- **Redness** and **warmth** caused by increased blood flow to the injured area.

Treatment for a sprain is in the form of RICE:
- **Rest** – the patient should rest and not move the injured part of the body.
- **Ice** – should be placed on the injury location for short periods (wrapped in suitable fabric to prevent ice burns) to reduce swelling and bleeding.
- **Compression** – gentle pressure should be applied with a bandage to reduce the build-up of the fluid that causes swelling.
- **Elevation** – the injured body part should be raised (to reduce blood pressure, which would then lead to less blood flow and swelling).

Physiotherapy

A **physiotherapist** specialises in the treatment of skeletal-muscular injuries. Physiotherapists help patients re-train or re-use a part of their body that is not functioning properly. This is normally achieved with various exercises to strengthen muscles that have become weakened.

For example, the following exercise programme could be used to treat an injured leg:
- Warm up the joint by riding a stationary exercise bicycle, then straighten and raise the leg.
- Extend the leg while sitting (a weight may be worn on the ankle for this exercise).
- Raise the leg while lying on the stomach.
- Exercise in a pool, for example, walk as fast as possible in chest-deep water, perform small flutter kicks while holding onto the side of the pool, and raise each leg to 90° in chest-deep water while pressing the back against the side of the pool.

Key Words

Diagnosis • Dislocation • Ligament • Sprain • Symptom • Tendon

Module B7 Summary

Energy Transfer

- All energy comes from the Sun.
- Plants (autotrophs) photosynthesise.
- Energy is passed up the food chain when organisms are consumed (by heterotrophs, e.g. herbivores or carnivores).
- Energy is lost from the food chain by heat, respiration and excretion.

Energy efficiency formula:

$$\text{Percentage of energy transferred} = \frac{\text{Input energy}}{\text{Output energy}} \times 100$$

- Pyramids of numbers show the number of organisms in a food chain.
- Pyramids of biomass show the biomass of organisms in a food chain.

Soil

Soil contains…
- biomass
- inorganic material
- air
- water.

Water content formula:

$$\text{Percentage of water content} = \frac{\text{Water mass}}{\text{Wet mass}} \times 100$$

Biomass formula:

$$\text{Percentage of biomass} = \frac{\text{Biomass}}{\text{Wet mass}} \times 100$$

Energy in Plants

Photosynthesis formula:

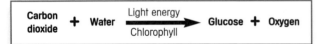

$$\text{Carbon dioxide} + \text{Water} \xrightarrow[\text{Chlorophyll}]{\text{Light energy}} \text{Glucose} + \text{Oxygen}$$

Limiting factors in photosynthesis:
- Temperature.
- Carbon dioxide intensity.
- Light intensity.

Glucose is…
- used to release energy
- converted into starch for storage
- converted into chemicals for cell growth.

(HT) Plants absorb nitrates from the soil by active transport, which requires energy.

Compensation point =
- the amount of carbon dioxide used in photosynthesis exactly matches the amount produced in respiration
- the amount of oxygen produced in photosynthesis exactly matches the amount used up in respiration.

Symbiosis

- Mutualism – both organisms benefit.
- Commensalism – benefits one organism; no effect on other organism.
- Parasitism – benefits one organism (parasite); harms other organism (host).

(HT) Sickle-Cell Anaemia

- **Hereditary** blood disorder, passed on by recessive allele.
- Beneficial in areas where malaria is common as sickle cells aren't infected by **malaria**.

Genetic Modification and Testing

Genetic modification process:

- Gene is isolated.

(HT) • Gene is inserted into target bacterium using a **vector**.

- Gene is replicated.
- Gene transferred to target organism.

Genetic testing process:

- DNA isolated.
- Gene probe created.
- UV or autoradiography used to locate the gene.

Respiration

Aerobic respiration — **with** oxygen:

Anaerobic respiration — **without** oxygen:

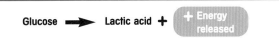

(HT) Anaerobic respiration produces lactic acid. More oxygen is needed by the body after exercise has stopped in order to break down the lactic acid — **oxygen debt**.

Double Circulatory System

- Blood passes through heart twice on every circuit.
- Heart has two atria and two ventricles.
- Three types of blood vessels:
  - Arteries.
  - Veins.
  - Capillaries.

ABO system: identifies blood types and enables donors to be matched to recipients.

The Body

Vertebrates have skeletons:

- Bones.
- Muscles.
- Ligaments.
- Tendons.

Joints move via **antagonistic pairs**. Can suffer from...

- sprains
- dislocation
- torn ligaments / tendons.

1 Say whether the following are heterotrophs or autotrophs. Write an **H** in the box for a heterotroph and an **A** for an autotroph.

a) Cabbage ◯

b) Human ◯

c) Elm tree ◯

d) Shark ◯

e) Ant ◯

f) Orchid ◯

2 What does the arrow represent in a food chain?

HT

3 What is the name of the process when a plant absorbs nitrates from the soil?

4 The three steps of photosynthesis are listed below in the wrong order. Number the steps **1–3** to show the correct order.

A Light energy is absorbed by chlorophyll. ◯

B Oxygen is produced as a waste product. ◯

C The atoms of carbon dioxide and water are rearranged to produce glucose. ◯

5 What are the three factors that interact to limit the rate of photosynthesis?

a)

b)

c)

HT

6 Choose the correct words from the options given to complete the sentences below.

respiration   compensation   commensalism

photosynthesis   genetic   light   carbon dioxide

The .... point is the point at which the rate of .... exactly

matches the rate of .... It's the point at which there's just enough

.... or carbon dioxide for a plant to survive.

7 Why is carbon dioxide called a greenhouse gas?

....

8 Fill in the missing word to complete the following sentence.

The relationship where two organisms both benefit from each other is called ....

9 Fill in the missing words to complete the following sentences.

A tapeworm is found in the .... of a mammal. Tapeworms have adapted to their role as

.... by developing a head with hooks and a .... surface area.

10 Give three symptoms of sickle-cell anaemia.

a) ....

b) ....

c) ....

11 The following diagram shows a bacterium. Match terms **A**, **B** and **C** with the labels **1**–**3** on the diagram. Enter the appropriate number in the boxes provided.

A Cell wall ⬭

B Cell membrane ⬭

C DNA ⬭

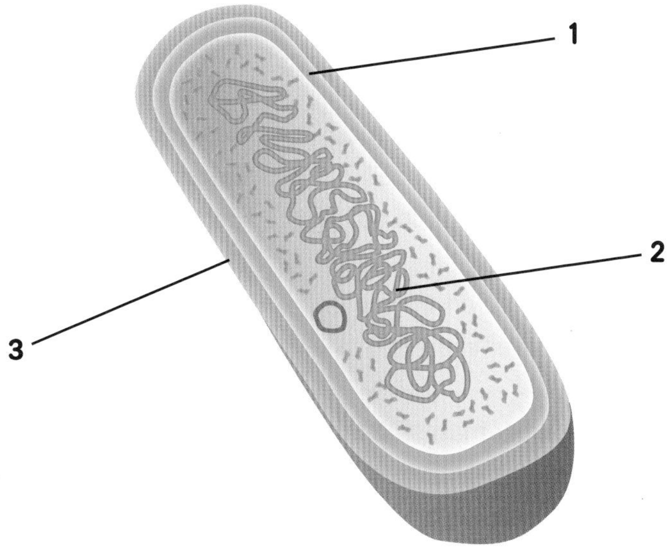

1

2

3

HT

12 What does ATP stand for?

....

Glossary of Key Words

ABO system – a way of classifying blood types.

Aerobic respiration – respiration using oxygen; releases energy and produces carbon dioxide and water.

Allele – alternative form of a particular gene.

Anaerobic respiration – the process of releasing energy from glucose in living cells in the absence of oxygen to produce a small amount of energy very quickly.

Antagonistic pairs – a pair of muscles that work together to create movement: when one contracts the other relaxes.

Antibiotic – chemical that kills bacteria and fungi.

Antibody – produced by white blood cells to inactivate disease-causing microorganisms.

Antigen – marker on the surface of a disease-causing microorganism.

Artery – a muscular blood vessel that carries blood away from the heart.

Asexual reproduction – new offspring are reproduced that are identical to the parent.

Atria – upper chambers of the heart, which receive blood coming back to the heart.

Autoradiography – using radioactive particles to locate a gene probe.

Autotroph – an organism that makes its own food.

Axon – the thread-like extension of a nerve cell.

Bacteria – single-celled microorganism with no nucleus.

Biodiversity – range of species in an environment.

Biomass – the mass of living matter in a living organism.

Bones – rigid connective tissue that makes up the human skeleton.

Capillary – a blood vessel that connects arteries to veins; where the exchange of materials takes place.

Carnivore – an organism that eats other animals; a secondary or tertiary consumer.

Central nervous system – the brain and spinal cord, allows an organism to react to its surroundings and coordinates its responses.

Cerebral cortex – the part of the human brain most concerned with intelligence, memory, language and consciousness.

Chlorophyll – the green pigment found in most plants; responsible for photosynthesis.

Chromosome – a long molecule found in the nucleus of all cells containing DNA.

Clinical trial – the process of testing a medical treatment or medicine on human volunteers for safety and effectiveness.

Clone – organism genetically identical to the parent.

Commensalism – a symbiotic relationship from which one organism benefits and the other organism is neither harmed nor benefited.

Common ancestor – the most recent individual from which all organisms in a group are directly descended.

Competition – the demand by two or more organisms for limited environmental resources at the same time.

Cystic fibrosis – a hereditary disorder that mainly affects the lungs and digestive system.

Denatured enzyme – an enzyme that has had its shape destroyed by heat and can no longer catalyse reactions.

Deoxygenated – a substance low in oxygen.

Diagnosis – the decision reached regarding the identification of a condition.

Diffusion – the net movement of particles from an area of high concentration to an area of low concentration.

Dislocation – the displacement of a part, especially the displacement of a bone at the joint.

DNA (deoxyribonucleic acid) – molecules that contain genetic information and make up chromosomes.

Donor – a person who donates blood or an organ.

Double circulation system – blood returns to the heart twice on each circuit of the body.

Ecosystem – a term that refers to a physical environment, including the conditions there and the organisms that live there.

Effector – the part of the body, e.g. a muscle or a gland, which produces a response to a stimulus.

Embryo – a ball of cells which will develop into a human / animal baby.

Energy – the ability to do work; measured in joules (J).

Environmental variation – variation that occurs as a result of a certain factor in the surroundings.

Enzyme – a protein that speeds up the rate of reaction in living organisms (a catalyst in living things).

Epidemiological study – a study of the factors affecting the health and illness of populations.

Ethics – the standards by which human actions can be judged right or wrong.

Evolution – the gradual process of adaptation of a species over generations.

Extinct – a species that has died out.

Fermenter – a controlled environment that maintains ideal conditions for microorganisms to carry out fermentation.

Fertilisation – the fusion of the male gamete with the female gamete.

Fetus – an unborn human / animal baby.

Food chain – a simple chain showing the feeding relationship between organisms in an ecosystem.

Food web – interlinked food chains in an ecosystem.

Fossil – animal / plant remains preserved in rock.

Fungi – group of organisms including mushrooms, toadstools and yeasts.

Gamete – a specialised sex cell formed by meiosis.

Gene – a small section of DNA of a chromosome which determines a particular characteristic.

Gene therapy – the insertion of genes into a patient's cells and tissues to treat a disease or disorder.

Genetic modification – the change in the genetic make-up of an organism.

Genetic test – a test to determine if an individual has a genetic disorder.

Herbivore – an organism that only eats plants, grass, etc; a primary consumer.

Heterotroph – an organism that is unable to make its own food; consumes other organisms.

Homeostasis – the maintenance of a constant internal environment.

Hominid – any member of the biological family Hominidae (the "great apes").

Hormone – a regulatory substance that stimulates cells or tissues into action.

Host – an organism that another organism lives off.

Huntington's disorder – a hereditary, degenerative disorder of the central nervous system.

Hypothermia – an uncontrolled decrease in body temperature.

Immune system – the body's defence system against infections and diseases (consists of white blood cells and antibodies).

Incubator – a container that controls temperature and oxygen levels to help premature babies to survive.

Insoluble – a substance unable to dissolve in a solvent.

***In vitro* fertilisation (IVF)** – a technique in which egg cells are fertilised outside the female body.

Lactic acid – a chemical produced by animal cells as a product of the incomplete breakdown of glucose during anaerobic respiration; can also be produced by the breakdown of lactose in yoghurt production.

Ligament – the tissue that connects a bone to a joint.

Meiosis – the cell division that forms daughter cells with half the number of chromosomes as the parent cell.

Meristem – an area where unspecialised cells divide, producing plant growth.

Mitosis – the cell division that forms two daughter cells, each with the same number of chromosomes as the parent cell.

Muscle – tissue that can contract and relax to produce movement.

Mutation – a spontaneous change in the genetic code of a cell.

Mutualism – a symbiotic relationship from which both organisms benefit.

Natural immunity – to remain resistant to or be unaffected by a specific disease.

Glossary of Key Words

Natural selection – a natural process resulting in the evolution of organisms best adapted to the environment.

Neuron – a specialised cell that transmits electrical messages or nerve impulses when stimulated.

Nucleus – control centre of a cell.

Organelles – the different parts of a cell's structure.

Osmosis – the movement of water from a dilute to a more concentrated solution across a partially permeable membrane.

Oxygenated – a substance rich in oxygen.

Oxyhaemoglobin – haemoglobin with oxygen bound on.

Parasite – an organism that lives off another organism.

Parasitism – a symbiotic relationship in which one organism benefits and the other organism is harmed.

Peer review – the process by which new scientific ideas and discoveries are validated by other scientists.

Photosynthesis – the chemical process that takes place in green plants where water combines with carbon dioxide to produce glucose using light.

Phototropism – a plant's response to light.

Protein – large organic compounds made of amino acids.

Pyramid of biomass – records the biomass at each stage of a food chain.

Pyramid of numbers – shows the feeding relationships between organisms in a food chain.

Receptor – the part of the nervous system that detects a stimulus.

Recipient – person receiving a donated organ or blood.

Reflex action – a fast, automatic response.

Ribosome – a small structure found in the cytoplasm of living cells, where protein synthesis takes place.

Selective breeding – the production of new varieties of animals and plants by artificial selection.

Sensor – detects a stimulus.

Side effect – condition caused by taking medication, e.g. headache, nausea.

Soluble – a property that means a substance that can dissolve in a solvent.

Sprain – a stretch or tear in a ligament.

Stem cell – a cell of a human embryo or adult bone marrow which has the ability to differentiate.

Stimulus – a change in an organism's environment.

Survival of the fittest – process by which the organisms that are best adapted to their environment survive to pass on their successful traits to their offspring.

Sustainable – capable of being continued with minimal long-term effect on the environment.

Symbiosis – a relationship in which members of different species live in close association with one another.

Symptom – a visible or noticeable effect of a disease, illness or injury.

Synapse – a small gap between adjacent neurons.

Tendon – tissue that connects a muscle to a bone.

Theory of Evolution – the most likely scientific explanation, based on evidence, as to why organisms are the way they are.

Urea – toxins produced when proteins are broken down.

Valve – a device that ensures the flow of a liquid (e.g. blood) in the right direction.

Variation – differences between individuals of the same species.

Vein – a blood vessel that carries blood towards the heart.

Ventricle – one of the lower chambers of the heart, which pumps blood out of the heart.

Vertebrate – organism with an internal skeleton.

Virus – tiny microorganism with a very simple structure that is reliant on using a cell's machinery to reproduce.

Zygote – a cell formed by the fusion of the nuclei of a male sex cell and female sex cell (gametes).

(HT) **Active site** – the place where the molecule fits into the enzyme.

Active transport – the movement of a substance against a concentration gradient.

ADH (anti-diuretic hormone) – a hormone that controls the concentration of urine.

ATP (adenosine triphosphate) – a chemical released during respiration; the 'energy currency' of living things.

Auxin – a plant hormone that affects the growth and development of a plant.

Co-dominant – alleles that will both appear if they are present.

Compensation point – the point at which the rate of photosynthesis exactly matches the rate of respiration.

Hypothalamus – the part of the brain responsible for maintaining homeostasis.

Oxygen debt – an oxygen deficiency caused by anaerobic respiration during intense or vigorous exercise. The 'debt' is the amount of oxygen needed by the body to oxidise the build-up of lactic acid produced during anaerobic respiration.

Pituitary gland – the small gland at the base of the brain that produces hormones.

Placebo – dummy medical treatment that is inert (does not work), such as a sugar pill.

Plasmid – unique to bacteria; made up of circular, double-stranded DNA

Pre-implantation Genetic Diagnosis – involves removing a cell from an embryo at an early stage of development and testing it for genetic disorders.

Sex-determining region Y – a sex-determining gene on the Y chromosome in humans and other primates.

Vasoconstriction – the narrowing of the blood vessels to decrease heat loss from the surface of the skin.

Vasodilation – the widening of the blood vessels to increase heat loss from the surface of the skin.

Vector – an organism (often a microorganism) used to transfer a gene, or genes, from one organism to another.

Answers to Practice Questions

Module B1

1. proteins
2. **a)–b) In any order:** Structural proteins; Enzymes.
3. alleles
4.

Offspring   BB   Bb   Bb   bb
             Brown   Brown   Brown   Blue

5. **a)** chromosomes   **b)** asexual   **c)** clones
   d) environmental   **e)** sexual   **f)** X
6. **a)** The central nervous system.
   b) i) Continuous, involuntary movement; Dementia.
   ii) Any two from: Weight loss; Troublesome coughs; Repeated chest infections; Salty sweat; Abnormal faeces.
7. Amniocentesis testing and Chorionic Villus testing.

8. True Positive – Fetus **has** the disorder – Fetus **has** the disorder.
   True Negative – Fetus **does not** have the disorder – Fetus **does not** have the disorder.
   False Positive – Fetus **has** the disorder – Fetus **does not** have the disorder.
   False Negative – Fetus **does not** have the disorder – Fetus **has** the disorder.
9. Bacteria and other **single-cell** organisms can **reproduce** by **dividing** to form two new individuals.
10.

Cell divides for   Each cell is
the only time.   identical to the
                        parental cell.

Module B2

1. **a)–c) In any order:** Bacteria; Fungi; Viruses.
2. Warmth; Food; Humidity.
3. **a)** Tears.
   b) Stomach acid.
   c) Skin.
   d) Sweat.
4. B, D, A, C.
5. **a)** White blood cell.
   b) Antibody.
   c) Antigen.
   d) Microorganism.

6. B.
7. **a)** There is a small chance of side effects occurring.
   b) The virus causing the disease mutates, producing a new strain that's unaffected by the current vaccine.
8. A, C, D.
9. To make sure that all the bacteria are killed and none survive to become immune to the antibiotic.
10. arteries; veins; fatty; vessels
11. A4, B3, C1, D6, E2, F5.

Module B3

1. 3500 million years ago.
2. **a)–b) In any order:** Cellular structure is similar; Genetic code is similar.
3. **a)** history; evolutionary
   b) Analysing **DNA** can be used to fill gaps in the fossil record.
   c) The more shared **genes** organisms have, the more closely **related** they are.
4. A, C, D E.
5. Environmental variation is when a characteristic is caused by the environment rather than by genetics, so the characteristic can't be passed on. **Accept any suitable example.**

6. mated; characteristics
7. **a)–b) Any three from:** Increased competition; New predators; Changes to the environment; New diseases; Human activities e.g industry, deforestation.
8. variety; resources
9.

| Oak tree | Greenfly | Ladybird | Blackbird |

10. **a)–b) In any order:** Hormones; Nerves.
11. A2, B5, C1, D3, E4.

Module B4

1. maintenance; constant; environment.
2. Death will rapidly follow.
3. B and C
4. A
5. **a) i)–ii) In any order:** Blood oxygen levels; Salt levels.
    b) i)–ii) In any order: Scuba diving; Mountain climbing.
6. **a)** A4; B1; C2; D3
    b) The maintenance of a steady state by reversing the change in conditions.
7. **a)–c) In any order:** Oxygen; Carbon dioxide; Dissolved food.

8. **a) and b)**

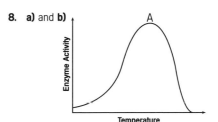

    c) It is where an enzyme is permanently destroyed and stops working.
9. Vasodilation – Hot conditions; Vasoconstriction – Cold conditions
10. C
11. **a)** Kidneys
    b) iii)
12. A small amount of concentrated urine will be produced.

Module B5

1. **a)** A Cell membrane; B Cytoplasm; C Ribosome; D Nucleus.
    b) Protein synthesis occurs.
2. A4; C3; D2.
3. **a)–b) In any order:** Testes; Ovaries.
4. Zygote
5. **a) i)** T **ii)** G **iii)** C **iv)** A
    b) mRNA is a smaller copy that is small enough to leave.
6. **a)** Three
    b) Twenty
7. **a)** They are unspecialised and can turn into any kind of cell.
    b) The cells will have become specialised.
8. Meristems
9. **a)** Responsible for transporting dissolved food up and down the plant.
    b) Responsible for transporting water and dissolved minerals from the roots to the leaves.
10. **a) Drawing needs to show a shoot curving to face the light**.
    b) The letter A should be in middle of the shoot tip.
    c) On the curved surface furthest away from the light, i.e. left hand side.
11. It makes them grow faster.

Module B6

1. **a)** Central nervous system
    b) Peripheral nervous system
    c) Central nervous system
2. **a)** Sensory neuron
    b) Motor neuron
3. It causes the gland to release a hormone into the blood.
4. **a)–b) In any order:** It insulates the neuron; It increases the speed at which the impulse travels.
5. Synapses are the gaps between adjacent neurons.
6. A4; B2; C3.
7. Stepping reflex – Baby makes walking movements with legs when held under arms in an upright position.

Startle (Moro) reflex – Baby shoots out arms and legs when startled.
Grasping Reflex – Baby tightly grasps a finger that is placed in its hand.
Rooting Reflex – Baby turns head and opens mouth when its cheek is stroked.
Sucking Reflex – Baby sucks on a finger that is put into its mouth.
8. C
9. **a)–b) In any order:** Electroencephalogram (EEG); Magnetic Resonance Imaging (MRI)
10. Feral children
11. They change the speed at which nerve impulses travel to the brain.
12. Ecstasy (MDMA)

Module B7

1. **a)** A
    b) H
    c) A
    d) H
    e) H
    f) A
2. The direction of energy transfer.
3. Active transport
4. A1; B3; C2
5. **a)** Light intensity
    b) Temperature
    c) Carbon dioxide concentration
6. compensation; photosynthesis; respiration; light
7. It traps heat radiation and prevents it leaving the Earth.
8. Mutualism
9. intestine; parasite; large
10. **a)–c) Any three from:** Eyesight problems; Anaemia; Joint pain; Painful cramps; Feeling weak or tired
11. A3; B1; C2
12. Adenosine triphosphate

Index